68325   QC
                               16
Rouzé   062R613

Robert Oppenheimer, the man and
  his theories

CHABOT
COLLEGE
LIBRARY

25555 Hesperian Boulevard
Hayward, California 94545

PRINTED IN U.S.A.

ROBERT OPPENHEIMER

ROBERT OPPENHEIMER

The Man and his Theories

MICHEL ROUZÉ

translated by
PATRICK EVANS

A Profile in Science

PAUL S. ERIKSSON, INC.

New York

Contents

SELECTED WRITINGS

ROBERT OPPENHEIMER

1

Early Years

THE life story of J. Robert Oppenheimer is by no means just that of a man or a scientist. It expresses and condenses, in a striking and significant way, a drama which is part of the times we live in: the novel responsibility of the scientist in his relations with the state, now that the advance of knowledge brings with it, not a slight increase in the power of military weapons, as it once did, but the danger of liquidating the human species and inaugurating a long eclipse of civilization. Oppenheimer's life presents an interest far greater than that of any one individual, however important. It is also much more than an episode in the conquest of nature by the human mind. It seems to have been chosen by destiny to help us in posing a problem, or rather a whole set of problems, the solution of which will determine whether we collectively survive or commit suicide.

J. Robert Oppenheimer was born on April 22nd, 1904, in New York. His father had come over from Germany at the age of fourteen and had subsequently made a fortune as a textile importer. He bought pictures and had built up a hand-

9

some private collection which included three paintings by Van Gogh. Thus Robert Oppenheimer and his brother Frank, his junior by a few years, grew up in the atmosphere of one of those Jewish families where the practice of business is combined with an ever active concern for intellectual and artistic values. Both boys eventually chose science as a career.

Their mother, Ella Freedman, who came from Baltimore, was not only interested in the arts; she was herself a painter and a teacher of painting. A delicate woman with refined tastes, she died young; Robert was nine years old. Her untimely passing left a great gap in his boyhood world. It is possible that in his later life the breadth of his cultural interests and a certain delicacy of taste and feeling were the means by which he sought to perpetuate his image of his mother.

Child prodigy. At the age of five Robert was a collector of geological specimens. His grandfather sent him a large number of interesting items from Germany. The collection grew to such good effect that when the boy was only eleven he was formally admitted to the first scientific society he ever joined, the Mineralogical Club of New York.

After attending the Ethical Culture School, Robert Oppenheimer became a student at Harvard University. At that time he was thinking of becoming a chemist—having discarded his first ambition, poetry, and his second, architecture. His studies were both classical and scientific; he learned Greek and Latin at the same time as physics and chemistry, and published a few poems. In a country where school and university education were already characterized by early specialization, which imprisons men in watertight compartments and leaves them ignorant outside their own field, this diversity in Robert Oppenheimer's interests was a sign of his genius. It was not dilettantism, the practice of which results in a spurious, merely superficial culture; his curiosity was genuine and deep, not untinged by anxiety and a nostalgia for such periods as the eighteenth century, when it was still possible for a man to hope that the exercise of reason would lay bare the laws governing the universe, including those which held the secret of happiness for all mankind.

Robert Oppenheimer astounded everyone who knew him by his appetite for work and his capacity for learning. One feat recorded of him was his reading the whole of Gibbon's *The Decline and Fall of the Roman Empire* during a train journey from San Francisco to New York. Western culture alone could not satisfy his mind; he delved into Buddhism and the Hindu philosophies and later set himself without hesitation to learn Sanskrit. Oriental thought appeared to him to furnish the glimmer of an answer to the questions which obsessed him about the relationship between science and the destiny of mankind. In his lectures and articles on such problems he sometimes alludes to the mystical systems of the ancient thinkers of Asia but does not make his meaning entirely clear; he seems in those passages to be touching on a somewhat remote, secret domain.

In 1925 he graduated from Harvard with the mention *summa cum laude*, after completing in three years a course which usually takes four. He then set sail for the Old World, with which his family still maintained numerous connections, and whose famous universities had not yet begun to lose their prestige to the richly endowed laboratories of the New. Many American students were going over to deepen their understanding of physics under the European masters of the subject, and to take part in the frontier researches which were leading our ideas about matter along entirely new paths. In addition to their native dynamism, these young men moved in the aura conferred by their fathers' dollars or by much ampler educational grants than those available to their European comrades.

Cambridge. Pioneer explorations of the atom. Oppenheimer first made his way to the University of Cambridge, where he worked at the Cavendish Laboratory under the direction of Lord Rutherford, the great British scientist whose pupils, without his knowing it, had nicknamed him "the Crocodile"—in his waistcoat pocket he carried an enormous watch whose ticking warned them of his approach and reminded them of the crocodile which had swallowed an alarm clock, in J. M. Barrie's *Peter Pan*. Since Rutherford's death in 1937 familiar use has been made, in British laboratories, of a unit of potential difference which does not figure in international tables of measurement: the *crocodile*, which represents a million volts. The nickname had the further advantage of exactly fitting the great scientist's irascible nature. His rages were formidable. He nonetheless took affectionate care of his "boys", as he called them. In 1933 one of them, the Russian scientist Peter Kapitza, arranged for the façade of the special laboratory which had been built for them in Cambridge to be adorned with a crocodile chiseled in the stone by the British sculptor Eric Gill. At the official opening Kapitza was asked the reason for the presence of this outlandish animal. He countered with an ingenious explanation: "Well, mine is the crocodile of science. The crocodile cannot turn its head. Like science, it must always go forward with all-devouring jaws."

Robert Oppenheimer soon distinguished himself among the "boys" by his talent for combining experimental work and theoretical inquiry.

Rutherford's laboratory was one of the high places of early atomic science. It was there that the British physicist had worked out, as early as 1903, his theory of the successive disintegrations occurring in radioactive bodies, the properties of which had been discovered by Becquerel and the Curies. Rutherford traced the full sequence displayed by uranium 238, whose successive disintegrations include thorium, radium, radon (an inert gas emanating from radium), and finally the stable, non-radioactive element lead. In the course of these spontaneous transmutations matter emits three radiations with clearly differentiated characteristics, which have been named alpha, beta and gamma. Rutherford and his fellow-workers discovered the true nature of alpha radiation, which consists of nuclei bearing two positive charges—in other words, helium nuclei—projected with an energy of several million electron volts. It then occurred to Rutherford to use these positively charged projectiles, the alpha particles emitted by radioactive bodies, in order to probe the electrical properties of the atom. In this way the entity discovered, the alpha particle, became in its turn a valuable tool for making further discoveries. Through studying the ways in which the radiation was diverted by different kinds of filter, Rutherford reached the conclusion that the atom possessed a very dense nucleus bearing positive charges which repelled radiation, and whose number was characteristic of each element respectively; one charge for hydrogen, two for helium, eight for oxygen, ninety-two for uranium. In an atom which was in an electrically neutral condition, the nucleus was surrounded by an equal number of negative charges, each borne by an electron. This picture of the atom, which was completed not long after by the work of Bohr, has been made enormously more complicated by subsequent discoveries; it has nevertheless remained classical and can still be used for explaining a number of the properties of matter. It cast an illuminating light on the periodic classification of the elements according to their physico-chemical properties, established empirically by the Russian scientist Mendeleyev in 1869. The number borne by each element in Mendeleyev's table simply expresses the number of positive charges of its nucleus and hence the number of its electrons, on which its chemical properties depend.

Rutherford went further still. In 1919 he realized for the first time the alchemists' dream, the artificial transmutation of elements. If nitrogen is bombarded with alpha particles hydrogen and oxygen are found to appear. Why? Some of the alpha particles (2 positive charges) penetrate nitrogen nuclei (7 positive charges), from which they expel 1 charge (a hydrogen nucleus), thus leaving 8 charges (oxygen nucleus). Man had succeeded in acting upon the tremendous energy— of unknown nature—by which the structure of the atomic nucleus was preserved. It is curious to note that Lord Rutherford, the modern alchemist, remained skeptical till the end of his life about the possibility of eventually harnessing on a large scale this nuclear energy of which he had been the pioneer investigator. Eight years after the death of "the Crocodile," his one-time pupil, Oppenheimer, was to be responsible for detonating the first atomic bomb.

At the Cavendish Laboratory the young American physicist observed the dogged struggle which the British scientists, like their colleagues in most other countries, were obliged to wage in extorting funds from the government or private patrons to pay for the increasingly expensive and complicated instruments which they needed for their experiments.

The journalist Robert Jungk (whose book, *Brighter Than A Thousand Suns*, has been one of the sources of information for the present volume) describes as follows the various pieces of equipment used by the Cambridge atomic scientists: "Investigators were accustomed to concoct them, with the help of their laboratory assistants, out of wire, wax and glass apparatus which they blew themselves. In 1919 C. D. Ellis, the English physicist, saw for the first time the experimental apparatus with which Rutherford had at that date just performed his first transmutations of atoms. Ellis wrote later: 'The whole apparatus was contained in a small brass box and the scintillations were viewed with a microscope. I can remember being surprised, in fact mildly shocked, that the apparatus was not more impressive'."

In 1932, in the same laboratory (which, however, had been considerably improved in the meantime), Cockcroft and Walton achieved the first transmutations of elements to be carried out by bombardment with artificially accelerated protons (hydrogen nuclei). Here is Jacques Bergier's description of their equipment: "To a physicist of today the machine used by Cockcroft and Walton would look like something bought in a streetmarket. They built much of it themselves. The laboratory was run on a shoestring, and a good deal of its apparatus was lent by a private firm, the Metropolitan Vickers Electrical Company. Walton had a grant from the British equivalent of the C.N.R.S.[1]; Cockcroft was employed by the University of Cambridge. Their equipment consisted of electric transformers capable of accelerating hydrogen ions to a degree of energy in the neighborhood of 700,000 electron volts (it will be recalled that the power of modern accelerators is reckoned in thousands of millions of electron volts). The two experimenters had no modern measuring instruments at their disposal. They measured voltages by making sparks travel between two aluminum spheres, each 75 centimeters in diameter, one on the ground and the other connected to the apparatus. Voltages were varied by adjusting the

[1] Centre National de la Recherche Scientifique. Walton's grant was from the Department of Scientific and Industrial Research. [Tr.]

setting of the alternator which supplied power to the trans-
former used for raising the tension. The transmutations so
obtained were registered by scintillations appearing on a
screen observed with the naked eye."

It is important to remember how these early atomic investigators had to fight (and Rutherford was a savage fighter when
he wanted to be) for the instruments without which their research could not have been carried on. This is doubtless the
reason why some of them were dazzled when the state, suddenly glimpsing the possibility of exploiting the atom for
military purposes, began pouring out money for scientific research. We can understand the powerful temptation to which
Oppenheimer was exposed when, during the Second World
War, he found himself being offered the most gigantic of
giant laboratories, a laboratory of which, a few years earlier,
no scientific man would have dared even to dream.

University of Göttingen. Quantum theory. While he was
at Cambridge, Robert Oppenheimer received an invitation
from Max Born, a member of the triumvirate then reigning
over the Georgia Augusta University at Göttingen, the other
two being James Franck and David Hilbert. Several centuries
of intellectual ferment had left their mark on the atmosphere
contained within the romantic ramparts of the peaceful Han-
overian town. Generations of Göttingen students had drunk
their mugs of beer and had dueled with swords, before turning into so many Herr Doktors for the benefit of their respective branches of learning. The collapse of the German
Empire in 1918 had left these traditions unshaken. Indeed,
some part of the respect which the middle classes had formerly paid to the Kaiser's officers was now directed toward the professors. Everyone at the University, whether
teacher or student, had a sense of belonging to an élite.

Celebrated above all for its mathematicians (the famous
Karl Friedrich Gauss had taught there in the previous century), the Georgia Augusta University, directly after the First
World War, had become one of the focal points of the revolution in modern physics. The quantum theory, created by
Niels Bohr, a Dane, had put the finishing touches to the
first picture of the atom: the electrons gravitated around the
nucleus in definite orbital paths, and every transition of an

electron from one orbit to another corresponded to the emission or absorption of a definite amount of energy, a quantum. This was not only an advance in our knowledge of the structure of matter and the origin of electromagnetic waves (of which one is light); it also marked the invasion of scientific and philosophical thought by a disturbing principle whose consequences were to be felt increasingly as time went on. The old adage, *Natura non facit saltus* ("There are no leaps in nature"), which had governed all previous representations of the universe, had been shown to be radically mistaken. The contrary was turning out to be true: physical phenomena at the atomic level proceeded only by leaps; they were fundamentally discontinuous. We are not even allowed to think of the electron gliding more or less rapidly from one orbit into another and passing through intermediate positions on the way; those positions do not exist. Having been in one orbit, or rather at one level of energy, the electron is found to be at another—not just any level, but one of the levels shown to be possible by calculations made in accordance with the rules established by Bohr; and at the same moment the atom either, according to circumstances, absorbs a quantum of energy or emits a light particle, a photon of a determinate frequency corresponding to the levels of energy involved. So we can understand Jungk's anecdote of a famous professor in Munich, who humorously remarked that a warning should be issued to all students wishing to enter the inner mysteries of physics: "Caution! Dangerous structure! Temporarily closed for complete rebuilding!"

The building was in fact not closed, but inside it a tremendous transformation was going on in a springtime atmosphere of creativeness. In Göttingen, physicists from various countries met at intervals to exchange news of their latest theoretical speculations or experimental results. Bohr himself came from Copenhagen to give lectures. No atmosphere could have been more congenial to Robert Oppenheimer, with his eagerness for discovery, daring generalization and intellectual adventure. In addition to physics he was still studying philosophy and literature, to the surprise of his colleagues. One of those who were most astonished by the many-sided personality of the young American was an English physicist staying in the same villa, Paul Dirac, who was already on the way to becoming one of the great names in theoretical physics. Following the line opened up in France by Louis de Broglie and in Germany by E. Schrödinger and W. Heisenberg, Dirac had set himself to tackle the various difficulties arising out of the quantum theory; there were some phenomena connected with the absorption and dispersal of light which the theory did not explain. Both in the lectures he attended at the University and in his day-by-day conversations with men in the forefront of fundamental research, Oppenheimer found himself among the advance guard of militant science on its way from conquest to conquest. The new conceptions which were producing a radically new vision of the world were being taught by the very men who were working out those conceptions, and the students found themselves invited to make their own contributions to the structure. "It was a heroic time," Oppenheimer was later to write of the days when the quantum theory of atomic systems was being worked out. "It was not the doing of any one man. It involved the collaboration of scores of scientists from many different lands, though from first to last the deeply creative and subtle and critical spirit of Niels Bohr guided, restrained, deepened and finally transmuted the enterprise. It was a period of patient work in the laboratory, of crucial experiments and daring action, of many false starts and many untenable conjectures. It was a time of earnest correspondence and hurried conferences, of debate, criticism and brilliant mathematical improvisation.

"For those who participated it was a time of creation. There was terror as well as exaltation in their new insight. It will probably not be recorded very completely in history. As history, its re-creation would call for an art as high as the story of Oedipus or the story of Cromwell, yet in a realm of action so remote from our common experience that it is unlikely to be known to any poet or any historian."

The German physicist Jordan recalls those years in the following terms: "Everyone was keyed up to a degree that almost took their breath away. The ice had been broken. . . . It became more and more clear that in this connection we had stumbled upon a quite unexpected and deeply embedded layer of the secrets of Nature. It was evident that quite new processes of thought, going beyond all the previous notions in physics, would be needed for the resolution of the contradictions—only later recognized as merely apparent—which now came to a head."

Robert Oppenheimer was thoroughly at home in such a climate of intellectual excitement, which offered a satisfying outlet for his gifts. He was not very strong (for several years he struggled with tuberculosis); he nevertheless poured out his energies unceasingly and took part in every discussion; indeed, once he had started talking it was not easy to get him to stop. It was his joy to please and charm others, to shine, to arouse sympathy and win people around to his side. Even at this early period a characteristic showed itself which was later to be both his strength and his weakness: he had the power of fascination and the need to exercise it, a gift which was naturally not without effect on the ladies of his acquaintance. Some of his less highly gifted companions even took offense and addressed a written petition to one of the professors, suggesting that the American be restrained from pushing himself to the front so enthusiastically.

But the professors, especially Max Born, were above any reaction of that kind. In Robert Oppenheimer they had recognized one of the most promising members of their noisy brood, a young scientist for whom they predicted a fruitful career. When the Prussian Minister of Education, because Oppenheimer had carelessly omitted one of the necessary documents in his application, refused to admit him to the examination for the doctorate, Max Born personally intervened to put matters right and emphasized the outstanding merit of the work submitted by the young American and the desirability of publishing it in the volume of theses composed at Göttingen. On May 11th, 1927, Oppenheimer took his *viva voce*. A doctorate at Göttingen involved passing a real examination, not just submitting a thesis. In all subjects except organic chemistry the candidate was marked *excellent* or *very good*, and his thesis was likewise pronounced *very good*; Max Born regarded it as a piece of valuable scientific work, well above the general level of doctoral theses.

During the following year Robert Oppenheimer spent some time at the universities of Zürich and Leyden. At the latter he astonished professors and students alike by delivering a lecture in Dutch only six weeks after his arrival.

In 1928 he returned to the United States. He had learned much and was resolved to advance to fresh conquests.

2

The Quantum Revolution

OPPENHEIMER'S role in the history of contemporary physics cannot be compared with that of Einstein or Schrödinger or the Curies—to quote only these three names. He has neither made any decisive physical discoveries nor achieved any original synthesis on the theoretical side. Yet he may well be the scientist who, after living through the quantum revolution in his youth, has succeeded in grasping better than anyone else its meaning and potentialities. He has investigated and experimented along several of the new paths opened up in the exploration of the properties of matter and radiation, and has published a large number of reports and studies. He has thus contributed much to the new edifice of knowledge, the creation of which has filled the first half of the twentieth century. A peerless teacher, he has become the foremost disseminator of modern physics in the American scientific world, and has shaped a whole generation of investigators. Finally, he has worked hard on the philosophical side, and this is perhaps where he has done most for us. The dramatic contradictions which confronted physics at the be-

21

ginning of the century were resolved only at the heroic price of abandoning some of our longest established and most dearly cherished ways of thought; this caused dismay not only in the main body of the scientific army but even among the leaders committing their troops to the assault on the unknown.

Even the greatest were bewildered. And when a human mind, even a scientist's mind, is overcome by bewilderment, it runs for shelter to the archetypes of pre-scientific thought, the lullabies with which our ancestors soothed their fear of an incomprehensible universe. When he had laid the foundations of wave mechanics, whose equations express the common nature of matter and radiation, did not Louis de Broglie write: "We may perhaps suppose that at the beginning of time, after the uttering of some divine *Fiat lux*, light, at first the only thing in the world, gradually condensed and so produced the material world which we today, thanks to light, can see. And perhaps some day, when time comes to an end, the universe will regain its original purity and dissolve once more into light."

In the new physics, the prediction of events on the atomic scale was proving to be a different matter from the prediction of events on the macroscopic scale, which is that of classical physics; the future track of a particle could be expressed no longer in terms of certainty, but only of probability. Some over-eager thinkers seized on this as a triumph for human free will over determinism, and claimed the formulas of the German scientist Heisenberg as evidence of this triumph. There was a danger here that laymen might get a wrong idea of the way science was tending. Oppenheimer has done much to discourage hasty and facile flights into metaphysics; he has assigned the quantum revolution to its correct place in the history of knowledge; and, while emphasizing that the increasingly specialized nature of scientific investigation prevents its results from being communicated to the world at large, he has been equally emphatic that the essence of the scientist's intellectual and moral experience both can and must be communicated, so that more people can become aware of their situation and destiny as part of the universe. A few years ago, when asked by a representative of a French daily paper: "Do you consider that present-day knowledge in theoretical physics proves what religions have long proclaimed, namely that there are insuperable limits to human powers of observation and judgment?", he replied: "The idea of scientific progress seems to me to have become indissolubly linked with the notion of human destiny. To me, this conception appears to be alien to religion. The development of science has underlined the discrepancy between the theoretically unlimited possibilities of knowledge and the limited capacities of mankind, between the infinite accessibility of the universe and our own immediate nature. The possibilities for knowledge remain unlimited, even if in future they are confined to a minority of more and more highly specialized researchers. Thus some of the abysses which, in the nineteenth century, seemed destined forever to cut us off from a unified vision of nature, have lately been crossed; recent work on the age of the earth, on the transition from inorganic to organic existence, on the properties of certain proteins which genetically transmit or preserve an acquired experience from one generation to another, and on the nature of nervous impulses, are so many bridges into the unknown."

Difficulty of creating new concepts. The great mutation of modern physics, which has made it possible to ask such questions as the one answered by Oppenheimer in the above passage, is not easy to explain in ordinary language. Our concepts have been hammered out over thousands of years of social relationships, and of experience of reality on the scale of our senses—the scale of a man chipping a flint arrowhead or turning a piece of metal on a lathe. These concepts turn out to be inadequate to express the relationship between a human observer and light corpuscles or elementary particles; only mathematical language will serve, and even that had to be drastically brought up to date for the purpose. But was not the human understanding faced with similar though smaller difficulties when, following Pythagoras, it had to be admitted that the surface of the earth was not flat but spherical? Herodotus scorned so absurd an idea and Aristotle received it cautiously, as a conjecture which could not be dismissed out of hand. Almost a century after Copernicus, Galileo narrowly escaped being burned alive for declaring that the earth was not the center of the universe.

However, thought patterns are not irrevocably built into us, like our genetic endowment. But we acquire them from our material and social environment in childhood and youth, and it is hard for us to throw off the influence of this learning process later on. In order to conceive of time as the fourth dimension in a space-time continuum, and to think of a particle as being at once a material body and a wave, we have to do violence to intellectual structures which have become firmly crystallized in our minds. However great an effort this may demand it does not seem to be impossible, and our descendants will no doubt find it progressively easier as the new concepts are assimilated into the cultural heritage. In this context a young physicist, M. Semon, recently pointed out: "A concept is not a mere association of ideas, it is more than a conclusion which coordinates facts. The assimilation of concepts by the mind takes place only in children and young people. In the adult it is effected only by effort, over a period of years spent in studying the concept from every angle, relating it to concepts already known, besieging it, and amplifying it by means of analogy. A concept is a complex of associations and meanings which is built up as part of the growth of consciousness. And its acquisition represents an increase in consciousness. . . . By acquiring and understanding space time and the corpuscle/wave, twentieth century humanity has increased its consciousness. This acquisition has now been definitively achieved, and it is striking to note that for the young people now leaving our universities space time and the corpuscle/wave are much more immediate and comprehensible realities than they were for their teachers, simply because they encountered them early enough to make them truly their own."

Until the end of the last century, space was regarded as homogeneous, time flowed uniformly throughout the universe, and the mass of a material body was an invariable magnitude. It is well known how these simple certainties have been shattered by relativity.[1]

In the same way, classical physics was implicitly based on the postulate that the phenomena of nature were continuous in character. Even if it was theoretically admitted that matter might consist of atoms, the scale on which material phenomena were observed made it unnecessary to take this

[1] See, in the same series, *Albert Einstein,* by Hilaire Cuny, translated by Mervyn Savill.

hypothesis into account in enunciating physical laws. In a conductor with a rising potential difference, the amount of electricity conveyed by the current went up in a continuous way. The energy radiating in the form of light from a heated filament also went up continuously as the temperature of the filament increased. Finally, since the work of Fresnel (1788–1827), scientists had abandoned (for good, as they thought) Newton's idea that light consisted of corpuscles, and had taken to regarding it as a vibration, a succession of waves; a hypothesis which accounted admirably for the phenomena of interference, and in general for all the known facts of optics at the time.

Nature is discontinuous. The continuity of matter was the first concept to begin breaking down. The progress of chemistry was giving the atom a concrete meaning. The study of the agitation of particles dispersed in a fluid medium (Brownian motion) showed that every little fragment of matter possessed an energy of its own; this explained, for example, the pressure exerted by a gas on the walls of a container; and the temperature of a body was nothing but the degree of agitation of the molecules composing it. As M. Jean-Louis Destouches writes, atomic science shook the structure of traditional physics but did not demolish it: "Instead of regarding matter as consisting of continuous systems, it was enough to consider every physical system as an assembly of smaller systems whose constituent entities could be represented as weights or spheres. Thus nothing had to be altered except the way in which bodies were represented; the principles of mechanics remained unchanged."

After the discontinuity of matter came that of electricity. Every electric charge is a multiple of an elementary charge whose value was ascertained by Millikan. When a potential difference is set up between two electrodes in a vacuum tube, the cathode emits material particles whose mass has been measured, and each of which bears this elementary negative charge; these particles are electrons, identical with those which circulate around the atomic nucleus.

Things got worse—for classical physics—when the radiation of the black body came under study. A black body, in the physics laboratory, is one which absorbs all radiations falling upon its surface, and itself gives off a radiation which is a function of its temperature alone. At every temperature the radiation yields a specific picture under spectroscopic analysis. At a certain temperature the radiation reaches maximum intensity at the red end of the spectrum; if the temperature is raised the maximum intensity moves toward shorter wave lengths (higher frequencies); everyone knows that a heated metal at first becomes dark red and then changes toward white as the temperature rises; gases raised to a high temperature emit a blue light.

Maxwell's electromagnetic theory of light made it theoretically possible to predict the spectroscopic analysis of the radiation of a black surface as a function of its temperature. Experiment agreed with the theory in the case of the longer waves (red and infrared) but not in that of the shorter. The German physicist and mathematician Max Planck showed that the difficulty could be overcome by postulating that the exchanges of energy between matter and radiation took place discontinuously: in light, energy travels in discrete quantities, indivisible *quanta*, whose value is constant for a given spectral frequency. For every wave length of electromagnetic radiation, the value of the corresponding quantum of energy can be calculated by multiplying the frequency by *Planck's constant*. This universal constant plays as important a part in physics as the number π in mathematics. If the physical data are presented in terms of centimeters, grams and seconds, Planck's constant is expressed by the decimal number zero point twenty-six zeros 655. Since the quantum increases with the frequency, it is naturally toward the violet end of the spectrum that the discontinuous character of energy most strikingly upsets the results foreseen by the classical theory.

Traditional physics accommodated itself to the material existence of the atom and even to the elementary electric charge; but the idea of a fundamental discontinuity in the energy of radiation was too much for it. The quantum revolution was, indeed, to assume dimensions which no one could foresee.

The next stage was accomplished in 1905, when Albert Einstein supplied an explanation of the photoelectric effect discovered not long before by Hertz. A metal on to which a beam of light is directed emits electrons. The number of electrons emitted depends on the intensity of the light, but the energy of each electron is independent of it; it depends only on the wave length of the radiation. Einstein advanced the idea that light consisted of particles or *photons,* each carrying its own quantum of energy. When a photon collides with an electron in an atom of the metal, it sometimes pushes it out of the metal, communicating to it an energy which obviously depends on the energy of the photon. The more intense the light the greater the number of photons and, therefore, of electrons expelled, but the energy possessed by each electron is always exclusively a function of the wave length of the beam of light striking the metal. This hypothesis was verified in 1923 by Compton, who discovered that when photons collide with a material body some of them are reflected with a longer wave length, in other words with their energy diminished. The Compton effect is explained by postulating that the photon has collided with an electron and has given some of its own energy to it, and therefore possesses only the remainder of its original energy.

So Newton was right after all: light is made of corpuscles. The spectrum of a dark surface, the photoelectric effect and the Compton effect had the further consequence of introducing a new notion into physics, that of *quanta.* And yet Fresnel was right too: it is only by regarding light as a wave that it is possible to explain the phenomena of interference and diffraction, which result from its wavelike nature. Thus there loomed in scientific thought a crisis expressed by the following glaring contradiction: according to which aspects of its behavior you consider, light is either a succession of waves or a stream of particles.

The idea of the quantum had only just begun its conquering march. After Rutherford had outlined his model of the atom—a dense nucleus of positive charges, surrounded at a great distance by small, negatively charged satellites— a major difficulty arose. According to Maxwell's laws of electromagnetism, the electrons orbiting around the nucleus ought to have emitted waves on a continuous spectrum and thus to have lost their kinetic energy and to have fallen on to the nucleus, the whole operation taking place in a very short space of time. But nothing of the kind happens. The electrons do not fall to the nucleus, and if the atom radiates this radiation is quantified: that is to say, for every chemical substance the spectrum takes the form of separate, discontinuous lines sited at characteristic wave lengths.

Niels Bohr revises the model of the atom. Clerk Maxwell's laws could not be given up; they had been brilliantly confirmed by a host of experimental results, such as the discovery of the Hertzian waves. As for Rutherford's model, it accounted perfectly for the deviations of alpha particles on their reaching the vicinity of the nucleus. It was at this point that Niels Bohr intervened; he proposed to solve the difficulty by introducing the quantum into Rutherford's picture of the atom. According to Bohr's theory:

(1) Electrons can move only in specific orbits forming a discontinuous series, whose distances from the nucleus are to one another as integers. There is an orbit of minimum radius. The other orbits have radii equal to 4 times, 9 times, 16 times . . . this minimum radius; in other words, the possible distances from the nucleus increase as the squares of the integers. The further an electron is from the nucleus the less strongly it is subject to the latter's electrical attraction and the more easily can it be detached.

(2) So long as an electron remains in the same orbit it does not radiate energy.

(3) Whenever an electron jumps from one orbit to another, it absorbs or emits energy. It absorbs energy in passing from an orbit near the nucleus to one further away, since in that case it has to overcome the nucleus' force of attraction; in the converse case it emits energy. Transition from one orbit to another corresponds to a radiation of a strictly determined frequency which can be calculated by means of Planck's constant. This is the reason why the spectrum radiated by a light-reflecting body is discontinuous: the photons do not carry energy in the form of a continuous stream, but in the form of quanta corresponding to the passing of electrons from one orbit to another. The movement of the electrons varies, of course, according to the structure of the atom, that is to say, according to the nature of the element under consideration; every body which receives energy (by being heated, for example) gives it out again by radiating on specific frequencies which are determined by its own composition. It is well known what brilliant use has been made of this property. The chemical nature of a body can be identified by studying the spectrum radiated by it; this is how astrophysicists identify the elements of which the stars are

composed. Sodium radiates principally in the orange-yellow region, neon in the red, and so on.

Bohr had thought in terms of circular orbits. Still working on the model which likened the atom to a miniature planetary system, Sommerfeld established formulas to cover elliptical orbits. Armed with these equations, physicists were now in a position, knowing the atomic number of an element (that is, the number of positive charges in the nucleus and consequently the number of electrons), to predict precisely in what orbits it was possible for the electrons to travel and what would be the frequencies of the radiation arising when electrons jumped from one orbit to another.

Louis de Broglie and wave mechanics. Applied to the hydrogen atom, which possesses only one electron, the theory coincided perfectly with experimental findings. The spectrum was exactly what calculation had predicted it would be. This pleasing harmony unfortunately ceased, however, as soon as attention was focused on the spectrum of helium, an atom with two electrons. Physicists were then compelled to resort to purely mathematical descriptions of the facts observed and, in doing so, to move further and further away from classical physical concepts. This undertaking, pursued chiefly by Louis de Broglie, Heisenberg and Schrödinger, led to the construction of a revolutionary theoretical system, that of wave mechanics. The new doctrine not only took account of the observed facts but predicted others, whose reality was subsequently confirmed by experiment; it also explained the majority of chemical phenomena. It was at precisely this juncture that Robert Oppenheimer began his period of study in European universities. Armed with wave mechanics as their "Open, sesame!", and with increasingly powerful instruments of observation, physicists were rushing into the exploration of the subatomic universe with the hectic daring of conquistadors setting foot for the first time in fabulous lands.

The basis of wave mechanics is the idea that matter, like light, is at once undulatory and corpuscular in character; or, to use Louis de Broglie's original terms, that with every corpuscle there is associated a wave. This holds good not only of photons, which constitute light, but of material particles such as electrons. The existence of a wave in connection with electrons enables us to understand intuitively why, in the architecture of the atom, only certain quantified orbits are possible; previously, whole numbers had made their appearance in physics only with reference to phenomena of interference involving standing waves.

Not without hesitation was it admitted that the electron, a material particle whose mass had been measured, must at the same time be regarded as a wave. But in 1927—the very year when young Oppenheimer was taking his doctorate at Göttingen—two of his fellow-countrymen, the physicists Davison and Germer, showed that a beam of electrons passing through a fine-mesh filter displayed diffraction phenomena in exactly the same way as a beam of light. But diffraction, a well-known phenomenon of optics, is inconceivable in a beam of anything but waves.

From the wave mechanics point of view, the Rutherford-Bohr model was no more than a kind of approximation, at best a picture serving to give us a first idea of the atom by appealing to concepts familiar from sense-experience. The real atom is more complicated. The nucleus is not a sun; still less are the electrons planets. Quantic values do not represent orbits, but lower or higher levels of energy. Moreover, wave mechanics differs from classical mechanics in not predicting the position of an electron at a given moment. It even proves that such prediction is impossible; all that can be calculated is the *probability* that an electron will be present at a given moment in a certain portion of space around the nucleus. This probability is proportional to the intensity of the wave in that region of space.

Must causality be thrown overboard? When they apply to an individual corpuscle whose characteristics can be subjected to measurement, most of the predictions of wave mechanics are expressed in terms not of certainty but of probability. Such is the case, for example, when the position and energy of the corpuscle at a given moment in the future are predicted. The introduction of this notion, probability, was a source of bewilderment, and made some people say that science was abandoning its hitherto inviolable principle, the law of cause and effect governing all natural phenomena. It would be truer to say that a new kind of causality was involved; the calculations leading to a statement of probability are no less rigorous, and no less accurate in their results, than those of classical mechanics. But they are certainly more complicated, and they make use of mathematical magnitudes which the world of sense-experience makes it hard for us to invest with any physical meaning.

Heisenberg, taking wave mechanics as his point of departure, gave mathematical expression to the *uncertainty relationships* inherent in the doctrine. Some of the measurements applied to the behavior of corpuscles are connected with one another in such a way that they can be carried out simultaneously only to a certain degree of precision. The more exactly one of these measurements is made, the less exact does another of them automatically become. Thus, the more exactly the position of an electron is determined, the less we know about how much it moves (and therefore about its energy); the more closely we measure its movement, the less we know about its position. This is not an inadequacy resulting from defective experimental procedures: it is a necessary consequence of quantum theory, from which it logically follows.[2]

"There are even" (Oppenheimer observes) "some odd things about the identity and the identifiability of the electrons themselves. That they are similar we know. Their inherent properties, their charge, their mass when at rest, are the same. We wish that we understood this better; some day, no doubt, we shall; but we know that it is true. But if classical physics were the whole story, we could still, if we wished, always identify an electron, and know it was the same as the one we had seen before. We could follow it, not, it is true, without trouble, but without paradox, without inconsistency, from where we first found it through its collisions and interactions and deflections and changes by keeping in touch with its trajectory. If it hit another electron, we would know which it was that came out in one direction and which in another. In fact, this is not really true, except in those special instances where the collision is of such low energy that the two electrons can be described by waves which never overlap at the same place at the same time. As soon as that is no longer the case, we lose in principle all ability to tell one electron from the other; and in atomic

[2] The *uncertainty principle* is the expression by which this startling aspect of Heisenberg's work is usually known in English. [Tr.]

physics, where the electrons of an atom, and even the electrons of neighboring atoms, are not well defined in position
and can often occupy the same volume, we have no way of
identifying the individual particle."

Thus quantum mechanics touches on realities of which
concepts derived from our macrophysical world can render
only an approximate or partial picture. One result of this is
the imprecision of the comparisons which physicists themselves use when they try to convey in non-mathematical
language some quantic magnitude with which they are familiar—s*pin,* for example. Spin, we are told, is the movement which a particle describes on itself, like the rotation of
a planet on its own axis. Yet not very like; for the physicist
is obliged to add that, in the case of the particle, the observer, in whatever position he may place himself, is always
in line with the axis of rotation. But how can that be? Was
it wrong to say in the first place that the particle turns on
its own axis, like a planet? "In reality," writes M. Semon,
"our error lies not in words, whose meaning we can always
enlarge or restrict at will, or in logic, since it is by means
of mathematics that this phenomenon, the spin of an electron, is susceptible of being correctly and consistently described. The error lies in our way of seeing; we try to
visualize an electron revolving, when in fact we are dealing
with an elementary particle which obeys completely new
laws."

There are plenty of other things to bewilder the layman
in the mathematical framework of wave mechanics. For instance, the wave associated with a system of corpuscles
does not move in ordinary physical space of three dimensions [3] but in an abstract space of a large number of dimensions. Again, equations describing the behavior of waves,
in this kind of mechanics, necessarily involve an imaginary
entity known as i, which is defined as the square root of -1.
But from a commonsense point of view no minus quantity
can have a square root, because all squares are positive.
And what are we to think of the uncertainty principle, which
defines with mathematical precision an imprecision inherent
in knowledge? We feel like exclaiming ironically, with the
poet,

[3] "Natural space," as it has sometimes been called. [Tr.]

. . . ces choses-là sont rudes,
Il faut pour les comprendre avoir fait ses études.[4]
[These are puzzling matters,
To understand them you have to have studied.]

Study, and advanced study at that, is indeed necessary if one is to grasp the structure of speculation and experiment which was being erected, about 1925, in the laboratories and lecture rooms of Cambridge, Copenhagen, Göttingen, Paris and elsewhere.

But we can allow ourselves to be more optimistic than Oppenheimer, in a recent statement: "Our knowledge today can no longer constitute, as knowledge did in Athens or 15th century Europe, an enrichment of general culture. It will continue to be the privilege of small, highly specialized groups, which will no longer be able to render it accessible to humanity at large as Newton's knowledge was rendered accessible." It may be that this pronouncement is partly based on a misconception as to what the principle of universal gravity did in fact mean to ordinary people in Newton's day. There is an essential difference between specialized technical knowledge, that of the man whose job it is to handle the latest intellectual discoveries, and knowledge of another kind, intuitive and diffuse, which we might describe as an attitude of mind favorable to the appreciation of those discoveries. There is no doubt at all that in our own day this second kind of knowledge is an indispensable element of culture. We live in a society which is conditioned more and more closely by the progress of science—both applied science and pure research; and this progress is accelerating so rapidly that anyone who is nearing middle age, and has learned nothing new since his school days, becomes a stranger to his own time.

This growing gap between school education and the advance of science within a single lifetime undoubtedly makes the spread of scientific knowledge far more difficult than it was in classical Athens or Renaissance Europe, but it also makes it far more necessary. How stupid are school curricula, which increase the hiatus by devoting so many hours to grammar and the Punic Wars, when twelve-year-old boys are fascinated by astronautics or nuclear fission and are

---

[4] Victor Hugo, *La légende des siècles.* [Tr.]

capable of taking in much more about such matters than their slow-moving elders imagine!

Back to America. Oppenheimer's skepticism concerning the possibility of incorporating the abstractions of contemporary physics into the general body of our culture seems to have become greater with the passage of time. This may be a result of his having taken part in the drama of the atom bomb, which eventually forced him to experience to the full the harsh dilemma facing the scientist in present-day society. We shall return to the point later. But we may imagine that in 1929, when he set foot once more on American soil, he felt no sense of isolation. He seemed destined to win one success after another in the career of his choice. The doors of America's universities were wide open to the young scientist; news of his European triumphs had crossed the Atlantic. British and German scientific journals had published papers of his on the application of quantum theory to intensity distribution in continuous spectra, the behavior of free electrons on coming into contact with an atom, and similar topics. He had the chance of choosing between several establishments which had invited him to come and teach physics to their students. After some hesitation he opted for the University of California, at Berkeley, near San Francisco. It appears that when he was asked the reason for his choice, Oppenheimer astonished the dean of his faculty by saying that he had been enchanted by the collection of French sixteenth- and seventeenth-century poets in the University library. This answer may have had something in it; but it is also a sample of the flippancy with which Oppenheimer's conversation is tinged, and which is part of his personal charm. Even when being asked questions about some serious matter he likes to answer in devious and sybilline fashion; but after a few such excursions his bewildered hearer is astonished to find that the answer as a whole, so far from evading the question, has illuminated it in depth by means of some brilliant, unexpected perception which reveals hitherto unnoticed relationships. An oracle or an apostle might have answered in the same way.

Having completed his course of lectures for the year at the University of California, Oppenheimer would go and teach at the Institute of Technology at Pasadena, near Los Angeles, and numbers of his pupils from San Francisco would follow him. They had no wish to be separated for six months from the youthful, slightly built professor, with his blue eyes and prominent eyebrows and his large nose pointing slightly awry, the teacher who communicated the new physics in such a way that it became a tremendous adventure of the human intelligence. "Despite his youth," says Jungk, " 'Oppie,' as they called him, soon came to be looked upon as a master and model by the rising generation of physicists in America, just as the great men of atomic research in Europe had been regarded by himself only a few years before. The veneration felt by the students for their hero was so great that consciously or unconsciously they imitated many of his personal peculiarities. They held their heads a little on one side just as he did. They coughed slightly and paused significantly between successive sentences. They held their hands in front of their lips when they spoke. Their modes of expressing themselves were often difficult to understand. They were fond of making obscure comparisons which sounded most pregnant and sometimes actually were so. Oppenheimer, himself a confirmed smoker, had the habit of clicking open his lighter and jumping up whenever anyone took out a cigarette or pipe. His students could therefore be recognized from afar in the campus cafeterias of Berkeley and Pasadena by their custom of darting about from time to time, like marionettes on invisible strings, with tiny gasoline flames between their fingers."

Month after month throughout this period of his career, Oppenheimer published important articles in learned journals both in America and abroad. And if his name is not among those of the great original researchers, he was nonetheless a marvelously active pioneer opening up the new regions discovered by others. It was a time when the intricate, fluctuating partnership between theory and experiment was especially fertile. The equations of wave mechanics promised a deeper understanding of the relations between matter and energy, and of the behavior of electrons and the structure of the nucleus. There were accelerators which enabled experimenters to use far more powerful projectiles than the alpha particles of natural radioactivity used by Rutherford. Means of detection were being improved. In Wilson cloud chambers electrically charged particles moving in a humid gas left a wake of tiny droplets, vapor trails which revealed their trajectories, showed where one particle collided with another and what transformations took place as a result. The apparatus, crude and imperfect to begin with, was soon sufficiently refined to register the smallest events in the sub-atomic universe and in particular the tremendous beams of cosmic radiation, which were among Oppenheimer's subjects of special study. Highly sensitive amplifiers made a count of the number of fast-moving particles passing through a small volume of space and gave information on the amount of energy lost by each of them, and thus on their nature.

As soon as they had learned the general structure of the atom—a nucleus, with its accompanying electrons arranged according to the laws of quantum mechanics—the scientist set about exploring the nucleus itself. The year 1931 was marked by a discovery of capital importance. When glucinium or beryllium was bombarded with alpha particles, it was observed that it emitted a powerful but unidentified radiation. Frédéric Joliot and Irène Joliot-Curie, by making this radiation pass through paraffin wax, found that in so doing it caused the appearance of protons, that is to say, of the positive particles which form the nucleus of an atom. The new radiation was thus so powerful that it not only expelled electrons from the atom (as do high-energy photons—gamma rays and X rays) but even pushed particles out of the nucleus. The discovery made a considerable impression, but through using inadequate equipment the French researchers mistook the nature of the radiation emitted by beryllium and glucinium. They wrongly supposed it to be an electromagnetic radiation consisting of photons, like gamma radiation. It was at the Cavendish Laboratory—which by this time was much better equipped than in the heroic years—that the British scientist Chadwick, encouraged by Rutherford, solved the problem: the radiation emanating from glucinium consisted of corpuscles having the same mass as the proton, but not its electric charge.

The discovery of the neutron, as the new particle was named, completed the Rutherford–Bohr model of the atom: Heisenberg put forward the hypothesis that the nucleus consisted of protons, which had a positive charge, and neutrons, which had no charge. This accounts for the existence of isotopes, which are different varieties of the same substance, with different atomic weights: their nuclei have the same number of protons and therefore of positive charges (this number gives them their chemical identity) but a different number of neutrons.

The exploration of the atomic nucleus involved physics in new difficulties. The force connecting the electrons to the nucleus was well known; it was the attraction between electric charges of opposite sign, as described by Coulomb. But the force connecting the protons and neutrons in the nucleus is neither gravity nor electricity. This force acts over very short distances but is nevertheless enormous, as is shown by the massive power of the means required to expel a proton or a neutron from the nucleus, namely bombardment with high-energy particles. Even now, the nature of nuclear forces is still one of the central topics of discussion in nuclear physics.

Among the notes published by Oppenheimer at the time mention may be made here of one which describes the transmutation of a lithium atom under the impact of a proton. The lithium nucleus, consisting of three protons and four neutrons, absorbs the incoming proton and consequently changes its own identity: it becomes beryllium, an element with four protons. At the same time energy escapes from the nucleus in the form of a high-energy electromagnetic radiation, namely gamma rays.

In the years preceding the Second World War many similar nuclear reactions were brought to light. Elements were transmuted into other elements by means of alpha particles (helium nuclei), deuterons (heavy hydrogen nuclei, each consisting of one proton and one neutron), protons, and neutrons. Energy was simultaneously liberated, borne by various kinds of particle or by gamma photons. Wave mechanics was the theoretical means which supplied the explanation for these reactions, and also the basis for all attempts to predict their nature and the species of the accompanying radiation. It led to the hypothesis of a previously unknown particle, the meson, with a mass between those of the proton and the electron, and a role in the field of nuclear forces comparable to that of the photon in the electromagnetic field.

On the eve of the war, Oppenheimer had an outstanding reputation as a theoretical physicist with an all-around grasp of the latest work in the subject, and above all as an excellent teacher who had trained a large number of young American scientists and who enjoyed a lively popularity among them.

Impact of political realities. As in his student days, he was incapable of limiting his interests exclusively to scientific inquiry. But now it was not so much medieval poetry and the Hindu mystics which preoccupied his mind, as the state of the world under the menace of Hitlerism. In the universities of Germany, which he knew well, the Nazis were driving out all scholars of "non-Aryan" descent and any of their colleagues who dared to speak on their behalf. In Göttingen, constraint and fear were replacing the free, zestful spirit of intellectual emulation. Most German professors bowed their heads before the powers of darkness; they were men better suited to a peaceful university career and a life of research than to political awareness and political courage. A few mediocre men—and two Nobel Prize winners, Lenard and Stark—had become active Nazi supporters even before the end of the Weimar Republic, reckoning on the advantages to be gained from hunting with the pack. They denounced as "Jewish physics" Einstein's relativity and even the quantum theory, Niels Bohr being only half Aryan. What a triumph of stupidity—there were models of the atomic nucleus which measured up to the demands of racial purity, and others which did not! Political dogmatism (in this case a particularly poverty-stricken dogmatism) was making brutal war on the fundamental postulate of all scientific endeavor to understand nature, namely that rational, objective truth exists and has rights which cannot be encroached upon by the needs of any ideology or social structure. This was not the first time that such a cloud had overhung the history of science; and in our own day we have seen the same thing happening in other countries. But the attack delivered by the Hitlerian State on free intelligence was especially savage. Many scholars in different countries felt threatened by fascism and were united in sympathy with its first victims. The latter included relations and personal friends of Oppenheimer. He had hitherto been more or less indifferent to political problems but he now had second thoughts, and in 1936, when fascism assaulted the Spanish Republic, he openly took sides. At the same period he met a student of psychiatry, whom he nearly married, and who put him into touch with the militant Communists of California. In 1937 his father, Julius Oppenheimer, died, leaving him a comfortable inheritance which enabled him to make regular donations to anti-fascist organizations. He himself wrote pamphlets and leaflets which were printed at his own expense and distributed by some of his student friends.

But his zeal did not take long to cool down. He had become friendly with a young biologist, and married her in 1940. Disturbing news from the U.S.S.R. about the tragic fate inflicted by Stalin on several anti-fascist physicists who had fled to that country acted as a cold shower on the Communist sympathies previously aroused in many Western intellectuals. Oppenheimer moved away from the Communist Party—of which he had never become a member—but he could not break off contact with those who continued to fight in its ranks or sympathized with it. Too many of them were personal friends; one of them was his brother Frank, whose studies at that period on cosmic radiation supplemented those already made by Robert.

Such was the situation which held the germ of Robert Oppenheimer's destiny, in 1939—a year which was to usher in two apparently unconnected events: German preparations for the invasion of Poland, and the discovery of uranium fission.

3

Uranium Fission

WHEN the neutron came on to the scene, new ways opened
before research into the atomic nucleus. To reach a nucleus,
invading protons or alpha particles, being positively charged,
have to be propelled with sufficient energy to overcome the
force of electrical repulsion. Not so the neutron; bearing no
charge, it has no barrier of potential, no force of repulsion,
to surmount. By discovering this particle Chadwick had,
in principle, found an admirable projectile for effecting transmutations. And in practice various elements, when subjected
to neutron bombardments, do yield reactions similar to those
produced by protons and alpha particles: the nucleus disintegrates and in so doing usually releases a lightweight particle,
and what remains is a nucleus with an atomic number adjacent to that of the original nucleus. But further investigation was to show that in the case of uranium the result might
be something very different: the nucleus with an extra neutron literally breaks into two lighter nuclei, both the chemical elements thus produced being far removed from uranium
in the table of atomic numbers.

This phenomenon was so unexpected that the first man to obtain it—the Italian physicist Enrico Fermi—did not at first understand what was going on before his eyes. He had decided to repeat the famous experiments by means of which the Joliots, in Paris, had recently discovered artificial radioactivity; but instead of the alpha particles with which the French physicists had bombarded elements, he elected to use neutrons. Some of the elements so bombarded became radioactive, which meant that transmutation had taken place in their nuclei. At an early stage in his observations Fermi noted a seemingly paradoxical fact, namely that this radioactivity was considerably greater if the invading neutrons were first slowed down by being passed through water or paraffin wax. But the possible consequences of this phenomenon were so far from being apparent to him that when he undertook the chemical analysis of the substances obtained by bombarding uranium with neutrons, he considered he had hit upon an element heavier than uranium, a *transuranium* whose atomic number was 93.

Today, element 93 is well known and has been christened neptunium. And it is in fact obtained by bombarding uranium with neutrons under certain predetermined conditions. Nevertheless Fermi was wrong. The transmutations he was producing were much more revolutionary than he thought: he had achieved—and he was probably the first man ever to do so—the *fission* of the uranium nucleus. But it did not occur to him that this was what he had done; it looked too improbable that a neutron could break an atomic nucleus apart when much higher powered projectiles (alpha particles or protons) were incapable of eliciting such a result.

Fermi's experiments were repeated by several other scientists and gave rise to some rather confused argument. A German chemist, Frau Noddack, was the first to glimpse the truth: "It would be equally possible to assume" (she wrote) "that when a nucleus is demolished in this novel way by neutrons 'nuclear reactions' occur which may differ considerably from those hitherto observed in the effects produced on atomic nuclei by proton and alpha rays. It would be conceivable that when heavy nuclei are bombarded with neutrons *the nuclei in question might break into a number of larger pieces* which would no doubt be isotopes of known elements but not neighbors of the elements subjected to radiation."

In Paris, in 1938—the year of Munich and the invasion of Czechoslovakia—Irène Joliot-Curie and her fellow-worker Savitch announced that by bombarding uranium with neutrons they had obtained a substance closely resembling lanthanum, an element whose position in Mendeleyev's list is remote from that of uranium.

In Berlin, Otto Hahn (who for years had accepted Fermi's hypothesis of transuranic elements) suddenly shifted his ground; with his partner Strassmann he repeated Irène Joliot-Curie's experiments, and was able to show that the substance related to lanthanum was barium. The atomic number of barium is 56, which means that its nucleus contains barely more than half the number of protons in the uranium nucleus (92). Thus the uranium nucleus was split into lighter nuclei, one of which was that of barium (it is now known that other elements can be produced from uranium in this way). Otto Hahn named this process "bursting"; the term "fission" was adopted not long afterward.[1]

The fission of the uranium nucleus caused a considerable amount of energy to be released, with simultaneous emission of neutrons. Before we show how this energy—contrary to Rutherford's prediction—was soon made available in a massive and indeed explosive form, and before we examine the part played by Robert Oppenheimer in that development, we must run a rapid glance over the discoveries which, in the months preceding the outbreak of the Second World War, indicated the possibility of *chain reaction*—that is, fission taking place in such a way as to produce further fission.

To begin with, what is the source of the energy released when the uranium nucleus is split?

When the mass of an atomic number is "weighed" with modern physical equipment, it is found to be slightly less than the sum of the masses of the protons and neutrons of which the nucleus consists. This difference or deficiency in mass corresponds to the amount of energy liberated by the forming of the nucleus; it confirms Einstein's famous equation on the equivalence of mass and energy. If the deficiency in mass of a nucleus is divided by the number of particles the nucleus contains, the quotient will be found to vary from one element to another: it reaches a maximum

[1] By analogy with bacteria, which reproduce by fission. [Tr.]

among the elements of medium weight and is smaller for the lighter and heavier elements. It follows that when the nucleus of uranium, the heaviest of the natural elements, splits up to form several medium-weight nuclei, the sum of the masses of these nuclei is less than the mass of the original uranium nucleus. The difference has been transformed into energy which is shared between the various kinds of radiation emitted and the movement imparted to the bodies brought into being by the fission; and among these bodies are neutrons.

Experiments conducted by Frisch in Copenhagen and Joliot in Paris, in January 1939, confirmed that the energy liberated was approximately 200 million electron volts for every nucleus split, as had been theoretically predicted.

We have seen that uranium nuclei bombarded with neutrons give off neutrons themselves, when fission occurs. So the next question is, where do these secondary neutrons come from? There is no mystery about this: all elements (except hydrogen, whose nucleus consists of one proton and nothing else) contain both protons and neutrons, but the ratio of neutrons to protons is much higher in the case of the heavier nuclei.

When a uranium nucleus splits, a balance of neutrons is left over in excess of those forming part of the lighter nuclei which the fission brings into being. Some of these neutrons, having been incorporated into newly formed nuclei, become protons and cause the emission of one electron from each nucleus; this is negative beta radiation. Others, however, retain their identity as neutrons and are expelled; these are (for the time being) free.

Atomic physicists alarmed by their own discoveries. This phenomenon—the emission of several neutrons for every uranium nucleus undergoing fission—had been announced by Joliot and his collaborators on one hand, and Haenny and Rosenberg on the other. A most disturbing idea then began to take shape in the minds of several physicists. If the fission of one nucleus in a piece of uranium produces several neutrons, each of the latter will cause the fission of an adjacent nucleus; each of these fissions will liberate several neutrons, which in turn—and so on. This was chain reaction, the possibility of which was predicted at approximately the same time by several scientists, among them Szilard and Joliot.

In passing, it should be recalled that neutrons are not the only projectiles capable of causing the fission of a uranium nucleus; it can also be achieved by using artificially accelerated positive particles. But fission by neutrons is the only method of any practical interest, because it constitutes a self-propagating process; it produces neutrons which act as projectiles to cause further fission without a further application of energy from outside.

The possibility of chain reaction was astounding and revolutionary for two reasons, of which the first was of a general order and the second was peculiar to the time at which this formidable discovery appeared on the horizon.

It was at once apparent that nuclear energy left all previously available sources of energy far behind. It was calculated that every atom undergoing fission liberated about 200 million electron volts. The combustion of an atom of carbon yields about fifty million times less energy than this. If, instead of making the comparison on the basis of an atom for an atom, we do it weight for weight (and of course a carbon atom is lighter than a uranium atom), we find that the combustion of 1 gram of carbon yields 0.0089 kilowatt-hour, and the fission of 1 gram of uranium 22,000 kilowatt-hours; that is to say, some 2.5 million times more.

Uranium is by no means a rare metal. The reason why it had not been very extensively mined hitherto was merely that its industrial uses were very limited. If the energy locked up in its nucleus was now within sight of becoming practically available, humanity would no longer have to fear the exhaustion of coal and petroleum deposits; the dreaded possibility of a shortage of energy would be postponed for several centuries. The atomic scientist was a contemporary Prometheus, stealing a new kind of fire from the gods.

But this fire might turn into a blaze and consume mankind. We must not forget at what juncture chain reaction became a real possibility in the eyes of physicists, namely the beginning of 1939, when every thinking person was aware that the Second World War must soon break on the world. For once, even thinkers and researchers could no longer ignore political contingencies. Many of them, including some of the most famous, had been driven out by fascism and had taken refuge in the United States, or, like Enrico Fermi, had gone into voluntary exile rather than serve a regime they despised. The fact that some German scientists had chosen to serve Nazism merely increased the horror inspired by Hitler in such men as Oppenheimer, who was personally acquainted with many German scientists and was familiar with the liberal climate prevailing in German universities before the "brown plague" had descended on them. What would become of civilization if darkness fell on the whole of Western Europe, and perhaps from thence on the whole world? What would become of the intellectual and moral values to which scientific men were attached, not only as men but as scientists? The answer to this terrifying question depended on the outcome of the war which lay just ahead. And the war would undoubtedly be won by Hitler if physicists presented him with the weapon of mass devastation, of which the theoretical possibility had become dimly evident since the fission of uranium had been discovered.

Atomic physicists found themselves faced by a problem which they could not evade without cheating their own consciences. On the one hand, by persisting in investigations which could lead to the liberation of explosive quantities of energy through the fission of uranium, they were taking the risk of creating an incomparably more powerful weapon than human beings had ever used for destroying one another; a weapon which might place the very future of the human species in the balance. But, on the other hand, to suspend their work or deflect it into some different direction would be to risk being overtaken by the handful of physicists who had gone over to Nazism; and in that case the new weapon would fall into the hands of the annihilators of all hope for a human future.

There is a story that Otto Hahn exclaimed, when someone mentioned during a discussion the possibility of exploiting nuclear energy: "That would surely be contrary to God's will!" At that time, the belts of German soldiers were fastened with a metal buckle stamped with the words *Gott mit uns* [2]. . . . The fact is—though it was not known for certain until much later—that the physicists who had remained in Germany directed their researches, for the duration of the

---

[2] "God with us."

war, into a path which could not lead them to the bomb.

The Hungarian scientist Szilard, who was a refugee in America, suggested to his fellow-physicists that they withhold publication of all details concerning uranium fission, lest the results so far obtained be used in Germany. And in the letter he wrote about this to Frédéric Joliot, he expressed a wish which showed by what a dramatic situation scientists found themselves confronted: "We all hope that there will be no or at least not sufficient neutron emission and therefore nothing to worry about."

But, a few weeks later, a crucial experiment by Joliot's team frustrated Szilard's agonized hope: the French physicists had observed the liberation of from 280 to 420 secondary neutrons in the fission of 100 uranium nuclei.

Isotope 235 and the conditions governing chain reaction. Much ground remained to be covered before anything practical could be achieved. In order to manipulate chain reaction it was necessary to gain a better understanding of the intricacies of the phenomenon; and this meant more fundamental research into the atomic nucleus. Once again it was Niels Bohr (still in Copenhagen, but destined soon to follow the exodus to the United States) who made the decisive contribution.

Why was it that, *in some cases*, the uranium nucleus penetrated by a neutron burst into several fragments, as if under the influence of an internal disequilibrium, instead of simply undergoing a transmutation like those already known, in which an element moved from one position in Mendeleyev's list to an adjacent position? In order to account for this the nucleus was hypothetically regarded as resembling a drop of liquid. A large drop, if burdened by the addition of more liquid, splits into two smaller ones; in the same way the uranium nucleus, the heaviest nucleus existing in nature, was pictured as undergoing fission when its charge was increased. This "model," the nucleus as a drop of liquid, facilitated the first attempts to express the laws of nuclear fission in mathematical form.

But the forces which determine the cohesion or disruption of an atomic nucleus are much more complex than those which unite or separate the molecules of a drop of liquid. And in order to predict their effects, the help of wave mechanics must be sought. If the neutron was simply a tiny material sphere whose behavior followed the laws of classical mechanics, the probability of its encountering an atomic nucleus would be small—so small that chain-reaction fission would be almost inconceivable. The diameters of the neutron and the nucleus respectively are minute in comparison with the space in which they move. A block of matter, which appears so solid to us—a piece of uranium, for example—is really a tract of almost empty space in which tiny particles are separated from one another by enormous distances, relatively to the size of the particles. A neutron propelled into it would have about as much chance of meeting a nucleus as a marble, thrown at random into a space containing marbles of which each was several miles from the next, would have of hitting another marble!

But particles are not merely endowed, as marbles are, with mass and movement; they must also be considered as being associated with a wave of definite length. And so, as Oppenheimer says, "Another consequence of the wave-like character of all matter is that, when particles with very low velocity and very long wave length bombard other particles of matter, they may interact far more often than if those interactions were limited to their coming in contact. *The very lack of definition of their relative position makes interaction possible, in some cases over distances characterized not by their dimensions but by their wave length.* This is the circumstance which, among many others, enables the rare Uranium 235, as it occurs in natural uranium, to catch up enough of the neutrons which fly about to sustain a chain reaction in an atomic reactor." (The italics have been added here; they are not in the original text of *Science and the Common Understanding,* from which this quotation is taken.)

We shall return to the last sentence in a moment. Meanwhile we note that this passage from a lecture by Oppenheimer explains not only why the "marbles" represented by neutrons managed to hit nuclei widely dispersed in space, but also why slow "marbles" ("slow" is a very relative term here) hit the target more often than fast "marbles": their wave length is greater. It is of the same order as the radiation of the nucleus.

To foresee what will happen after the neutron has been captured by the nucleus is a rather more complicated matter, as we may suspect from what we know of the principles of quantum mechanics. In the complex edifice of an atomic nucleus, the arrival of an extra neutron, bearing a certain quantity of energy, can give rise to various phenomena: the mass of the nucleus may be augmented without a change in the number of protons, and hence without transmuting one element into another; or transmutation may take place through negative beta radiation and the transformation of a neutron into a proton; or the nucleus may undergo fission and neutrons be emitted. The probability of one outcome or another, respectively, depends on the energy level of the incident neutron and the internal energy levels of the nucleus. The determining factor is the correspondence between the energy of the neutron and one of the energy levels in the nucleus.

In order to insure fission and preclude the other possible results, it was therefore necessary to determine, both theoretically and experimentally, the right energy level for the incident neutrons. It was necessary to know the energy levels of the neutrons arising from fission—energies of which a precise spectrum picture had to be obtained—and, if possible, to reduce these energy levels, slow the neutrons down, so as to bring as many as possible of them to the optimum level.

As we have said, the probability that the nucleus will react in one way, rather than another, after capturing a neutron, also depends on the energy levels within the nucleus. Now, for a given element, these levels vary from one isotope to another. Natural uranium is a mixture in very unequal proportions of isotope 238 (92 protons, 146 neutrons) and isotope 235 (92 protons, 143 neutrons). It was Bohr, once again, who showed by calculation that the part susceptible to fission by bombardment with slow neutrons was isotope 235—much the rarer of the two, since it forms only one 140th part of the whole.

There are three reasons why it is possible to trigger off a chain reaction in a mass of uranium:

(1) Because it contains one 140th part of the fissile isotope (U 235).

(2) Because uranium 238, which captures slow neutrons without undergoing fission, behaves less simply with regard to fast neutrons (which arise from the fission of adjacent nuclei). In most cases these neutrons are merely captured, but in some cases fission takes place.

(3) Because the capture of a neutron by a nucleus of uranium 238 gives uranium 239, a short-lived, radioactive isotope; this transmutes into element 93 (neptunium), which in turn transmutes into element 94 (plutonium). And the plutonium produced in this way is itself fissile in the same way as uranium 235, through bombardment by slow neutrons.

For fission to set off chain reactions in several directions at once, it is enough that every nucleus split should give off, on an average, more than one nucleus capable of causing further fission. But it is obvious that this *multiplication factor* will be higher in a wholly fissile mass than in natural uranium. The procedure suitable for a pile, where the object is a controlled release of energy, is of no use in the case of a bomb, where the object is the rapid release—as nearly instantaneous as possible—of the whole of the available energy.

Consequently the men who, in 1939, bent their minds to constructing the nuclear bomb, found themselves facing a major technical difficulty: that of extracting isotope 235 from natural uranium.

An equally important task was to discover the *critical mass*. In any bit of uranium, a certain number of fissions are always going on which are capable of starting chain reaction spontaneously; but the reaction takes place only if the multiplication factor is greater than 1, and this cannot arise if too many neutrons escape to the outside instead of being captured. Obviously, the neutrons have all the more chance of escaping if they are emitted close to the surface. Those emitted deeper inside the metal rebound from the nuclei in their proximity, and, after a series of such impacts has slowed them down enough, reach the energy level which renders them susceptible of capture. Thus there exists a critical mass; when this is exceeded, chain reaction develops spontaneously. If this fact had been overlooked when fissile materials began to be extracted and stored in significant amounts, the first atomic explosion would have taken place

in the factory itself! The physicists also realized that in order
to explode the bomb it would be enough, at the fatal moment, to bring together two sub-critical masses, the sum of
which was greater than the critical mass.

All these things are classical now. But they had to be repeated here so as to show what a puzzle the scientists had
set themselves by deciding to make the bomb. And there
were still endless other difficulties to be got over.

Enter Oppenheimer. It was in summer 1939 that the god
of war laid his heavy hand on the cradle of nuclear energy,
then still in its infancy. By one of fate's ironies, the two
men who caused the decision were Leo Szilard, who had apprehended the possibility of chain reaction as a catastrophe,
and Albert Einstein, who was a pacifist. The first prevailed
on the second to call the attention of the United States
Government to the danger which would threaten humanity if the Nazis succeeded in building a nuclear bomb.
In view of this, Einstein asked the authorities in Washington
to speed atomic research by massive financial support, and
to secure an undertaking from the Belgian Government that
the considerable stock of uranium derived from deposits in
the Congo would be kept out of Hitler's hands.

American military men, conservative like military men the
world over, paid little heed to these warnings from intellectuals who talked of an unknown weapon born of the equations of a few university professors. President Roosevelt
himself was slow to be convinced. An added source of mis-
trust among official circles was the fact that most of the
atomic scientists working in the United States were refugees,
and so were aliens or recently naturalized Americans. Research was nevertheless stepped up, initially in a sporadic
fashion, in the university laboratories of Columbia (New
York), Princeton, Berkeley and Chicago. On December 6th,
1941—the day before Pearl Harbor—the White House decided to allocate large funds to the creation of a nuclear
weapon.

As early as 1939, Robert Oppenheimer had been particularly interested in uranium fission and the problem of
the bomb. He was very well aware of the scope and value
of the discoveries made in European laboratories. Although
he had given up all political activity at the time, the thought

of a Nazi victory horrified him as deeply as it did the refugee scientists in America.

Shortly before the outbreak of war, Niels Bohr visited Washington to give a lecture on the recent work of Otto Hahn. A brief report was telegraphed to the secretary of the physics faculty at the University of California. As soon as he had read it, Oppenheimer plunged into calculations in an attempt to work out the critical mass. For two years, while he went on with his teaching duties, the problem was never far from his mind.

In the radiation laboratory of the University of California, the physicist Ernest O. Lawrence, the inventor of the cyclotron (a machine for accelerating particles), was working to produce a process for extracting uranium 235.

As many people know, it is impossible to separate the isotopes of an element by any chemical process: they have identical affinities, enter into the same chemical combinations and are therefore not to be distinguished by any chemical reagent. Each differs from the other only in the mass of its nucleus, which is greater or smaller according to the number of neutrons. The only solution is to look for physical procedures which will differentiate between the isotopes by means of this discrepancy in mass. In the lighter elements, the difference between the atomic weights of two isotopes may be large: for example, the mass of the "heavy hydrogen" atom (hydrogen 2, or deuterium), whose nucleus consists of 1 proton and 1 neutron, is approximately double that of ordinary hydrogen (hydrogen 1), which has only a proton. But at the other end of Mendeleyev's table, a few neutrons more or less account for only a fraction of the atom's total mass. So the separation of the isotopes, difficult enough in the case of the light elements, becomes an almost impossible task in that of the heavy ones, and a wealth of patience and technical ingenuity was demanded.

Lawrence, at Berkeley, had set out to separate isotopes 235 and 238 in natural uranium by applying the principle of the mass spectrograph, a laboratory device for measuring the mass of an atom. The atoms, previously ionized, are accelerated by an electric field; they then enter a magnetic field which causes them to describe semicircles in a plane perpendicular to the direction of the field. The radii of these trajectories being proportional to the products of the mass by the speed, the light ions describe semicircles of smaller radius than the heavy ions. If this state of affairs is projected on to a photographic plate, each species of atom is represented by a short straight line; the whole set of such lines, representing the element's isotopes, is arranged like a spectrum; hence the term "mass spectrograph." If suitable collectors are used instead of a plate it is possible to gather the isotopes separately. But the quantities isolated by a mass spectrograph are in the order of a millionth of a gram per day, and the question was to produce uranium 235 in kilograms! To magnify the spectrograph technique involved numerous difficulties. The gaseous component of uranium is extremely inconvenient to handle, and the presence of a large stream of ions causes electrical phenomena which interfere with the separation of the isotopes.

Oppenheimer willingly offered Lawrence his help, and discovered a method which reduced the cost of the technique by between 50% and 75%. This led to the construction of the calutron (California University Cyclotron), which was used at the giant factory at Oak Ridge along with other methods of isotope-separation.

The help voluntarily given by Professor Oppenheimer to the men entrusted with the task of creating the nuclear weapon did not go unappreciated. In autumn 1941 the physicist Arthur H. Compton, a Nobel Prize winner, had asked him to participate in the work of a special commission of the National Academy of Sciences which spent two years discussing applications of nuclear power. Two months later this occasional participation became permanent cooperation, and in July Oppenheimer took charge of a small group of scientists who were strenuously discussing the theoretical nature of the best kind of nuclear bomb. It was during this period and in this group that, for the first time, serious study was devoted to the possibility of liberating nuclear energy in an opposite way to that of uranium fission: the *fusion* of light nuclei, such as those of hydrogen. We have seen that the lack of mass in the nucleus reaches its maximum in the medium-weight elements, about the middle of Mendeleyev's table. That is why fission of the heaviest nuclei into medium nuclei liberates energy; the energy released corresponds to the mass lost. If, passing to the other end of the table, a way is found of fusing light nuclei (such as those of hydrogen), so as to create heavier elements, there is likewise a loss of mass and a release of energy. This is the type of reaction which engenders the energy radiated by the sun and other stars. Oppenheimer and his collaborators decided that while it was possible in theory to realize explosive nuclear fusion, in practice the idea involved too many unknown factors; it must be shelved for the time being.

The United States had entered the war, time was pressing, the possibility of making a uranium bomb was becoming more definite with every day that passed; and the first belligerent who did make it would be sure of a crushing victory.

In August 1942, after an agreement had been concluded with the British Government, the United States Army was given official responsibility for organizing the work of British and American scientists to achieve the military use of nuclear energy, and the whole activity was named the Manhattan Project.

This centralization was in line with Oppenheimer's personal views. Indeed, he felt it should not be confined to the administrative plane alone. His work on the enterprise had convinced him that precious time was being lost because of the distances and lack of coordination between laboratories and research centers. Identical experiments were being conducted in different establishments; theoretical physicists had to leave their own places of work in order to study the results; the countless technical problems, solutions to all of which were required for constructing the bomb, were in the hands of workers scattered over the United States, Canada and Great Britain. Oppenheimer considered it necessary to concentrate all these men and their equipment in a single group of laboratories, an atomic community, where specialists in all the disciplines concerned would work in a unified command.

He convinced Compton and the responsible military authorities that he was right.

In autumn 1942, General Groves, the commander of the Manhattan Project, met Oppenheimer in a reserved compartment of a train traveling from Chicago to the Pacific coast, and proposed that Oppenheimer himself should take charge of the unique laboratory from which the bomb was to come.

4

The Bomb Township

WHEN he was summoned to direct the super-laboratory
which was to produce the nuclear bomb, Robert Oppenheimer was only thirty-eight. He was a brilliant academic
figure; he had published numerous studies on the most diverse aspects of the new physics, and he was probably the
man who had done most in the United States to foster the
rise of a new generation of scientists. But he had not distinguished himself by any major original discovery, as had,
for example, Enrico Fermi—to name but one of the many
acknowledged creative personalities who were to work under
his direction. Consequently General Groves, as soon as he
had announced his choice, found himself under fire; he recalls, "I was reproachfully told that only a Nobel Prize
winner or at least a somewhat older man would be able to
exercise sufficient authority over the many 'prima donnas'
concerned. But I stuck to Oppenheimer and his success
proved that I was right. No one else could have done what
that man achieved."

Oppenheimer, in fact, was just the right man. It is true

that a theorist of genius or an experimenter with some special approach, backed by the material facilities and vast funds placed at the disposal of the assembled scientists by the richest country in the world, might have achieved a spectacular advance in nuclear physics. But that was not the aim; the problem was not one of fundamental research, but of translating recent knowledge into a gigantic practical application. There were many technical difficulties to be solved, and there was the considerable task of coordinating the whole effort; but that was all. One reads nowadays that the war stimulated nuclear research in the United States. But this belief confuses science with technology. Oppenheimer himself has emphasized strongly that the war halted the advance of science, to such a degree that physics was no longer taught in the universities and the training of future scientists was held up for several years. The young men who might have entered science had departed for the theaters of war, and the ablest professors were working on the bomb.

Oppenheimer, as a physicist, had the special advantage of being at once an expert and an all-arounder. Never having been confined to a single line of research, he had a thorough knowledge of the results obtained in all fields. His clear mind comprehended the sum of what had been discovered so recently about uranium fission, and could see the possible links and extensions in this new knowledge. Above all things, he was an organizer and trainer of other men. His gift of personal fascination, to which all who have known him bear witness, was now to be put to the service of a concrete enterprise. And what an enterprise! He was to create and direct the greatest laboratory ever known, and from it was to come a superhuman weapon to overthrow the forces of evil.

There has been much discussion of the reasons which prompted Oppenheimer to accept the Army's offer, and indeed to hurl himself at his task with an enthusiasm which, on more than one occasion, endangered his precarious health. "His achievements might be considered exceptional by the academic world," writes Jungk. "But in his own more critical eyes he had not done enough. And since he was aware that, as past experience had shown, it was nearly always the young, who were still capable of radical thinking, who hit on new ideas, he was bound, as his fortieth year approached, to consider that he had failed to realize his highest hopes.

"At this stage he was suddenly offered an opportunity to accomplish something exceptional in quite another direction. He was invited to take charge of the construction of the mightiest weapon of all time."

We must be just. Among the atomic scientists of all nationalities who were then in Great Britain, Canada and the United States, there was probably not one who, having been offered the task, and feeling himself capable of carrying it through, would not have accepted it and devoted himself to it with as much conviction as Oppenheimer. The path of duty looked plain enough. Nazism had submerged all Europe and, if it armed itself with the bomb, would submerge the rest of the world as well; so the Allies had to make the bomb before the Nazis could. Einstein himself, in March 1940, had addressed a second letter to the Government in Washington, calling attention to the increased interest which uranium had aroused in Germany since the beginning of the war.

It must be admitted that the realization of the Manhattan Project was to influence Oppenheimer's personality profoundly; in a sense, the monster devoured the man who brought it to birth. That is another story, and we shall return to it later. But what scientist, having been entrusted with the same task, would not have ended by playing the sorcerer's apprentice?

A site had to be chosen for the projected super-laboratory. Oppenheimer suggested to General Groves the plateau of Los Alamos, in New Mexico. It was a desolate place, remote both from the Atlantic coast, where German submarines sometimes landed spies, and from any inhabited district, whose inhabitants might have been endangered by any accident occurring during experiments. Oppenheimer knew the ground well: the only building on it was a school to which he had been sent as a boy—psychologists, indeed, will doubtless assert that his choice was not fortuitous. The school was commandeered, and a few days later a team of workers arrived to clear "the hill." General Groves reckoned on having to house about a hundred scientists and their families near the laboratories, and auxiliary personnel. After a year, 3,500 people were living and working at

Los Alamos, and the population of the Bomb Township subsequently varied between 6,000 and 9,000.

Atomic scientists and military security. Oppenheimer's first task was to recruit his scientific team. This was no small matter. He traveled thousands of miles by air and rail to make personal contact with the men he had decided to enroll, and used all his charm to persuade them to come and settle with their families in the New Mexican desert. They had to sign a contract valid for the duration of the war and to live henceforth at Los Alamos, more or less cut off from the outside world. Against this, they would have the satisfaction of taking part in a stupendous enterprise and belonging to an unprecedented scientific community. Oppenheimer managed to inspire them with his own excitement. In spring 1943 the first atomic scientists arrived in the ancient city of Santa Fé, the former residence of the Spanish viceroys, from which they were taken every day by coach to the Los Alamos plateau until their living quarters had been put up.

The atmosphere in this nascent community was not unlike the youthful gaiety of a students' gathering. The tense, exciting conferences, at which the organization of the common task was sketched out, were followed by excursions and hilarious evenings. But this happy freedom was ringed around by the most remorseless of constraining influences, the machinery of military security. Oppenheimer knew this better than anyone.

Until the beginning of 1939, the scientists of all countries had been like one large family. Discord and even rivalry rose up sometimes—as they do in all families. But the dominant features were friendly emulation and a spirit of mutual help in the common struggle for knowledge. International gatherings brought the physicists together from time to time. The results of experimental and theoretical research were regularly communicated to scientific societies and published in specialized journals. Every forward step achieved in Rome or Copenhagen was immediately adopted to advantage in Paris or Cambridge. The idea of a scientific secret would have been unthinkable, something opposed to the very foundations of science.

The first blow to these sacred principles was dealt in November 1938, when Szilard suggested to Fermi that scientists themselves should impose a voluntary censorship on the publication of their researches into uranium fission, so as to prevent their results from being used in German laboratories. It was precisely because such a suggestion was shocking to scientific men that most of them received it rather ill. But in February 1939, the American physicist Bridgeman announced in the journal *Science* that, with regret, he would refuse to allow any scientist from a totalitarian state to have access to his laboratory. "The citizen of such a state," he said, "is no longer a free individual, but may be compelled to engage in any activity whatever to advance the purpose of that state. . . . Cessation of scientific intercourse with totalitarian states serves the double purpose of making more difficult the issues of scientific information of these states and of giving the individual opportunity to express abhorrence of their practices."

In 1942, as we have said, Roosevelt and Churchill decided that the efforts of British and American atomic scientists to create a nuclear weapon should be concentrated in the United States. Control was vested in a mixed group consisting of two generals, one admiral and only two scientific men. The Manhattan Project was set in motion in August and the undertaking passed irrevocably into the hands of the Army; the scientists concerned were thus placed under military discipline, their primary obligation being to maintain absolute secrecy about their research.

Most of them admitted this secrecy was essential; some of them, indeed, had been the first to insist on it. They found it less easy to understand why the military should erect walls of silence not only externally but internally, between the various groups engaged on the project. Each research section had to work in ignorance of what the others were doing, and a good many of the technicians employed at Los Alamos were unaware, at least initially, that they were taking part in the manufacture of an atomic bomb. Coordination was effected only at the top, in line with the best principles of military hierarchy. Such methods, though defensible enough on security grounds, were certainly not the most fruitful way of producing scientific results. So they were constantly evaded, and clashes occurred on more than one occasion between the scientists and their uniformed patrons.

The security section of the Manhattan Project, under the command of a colonel, vigilantly inquired into the past and present activities, the private life and political opinions, of every individual participant. No one could walk in the street, enter a shop or visit a friend without his movements being watched and recorded. Security personnel opened letters and listened in on telephone conversations. The most important workers, and any who were under suspicion for one reason or another, were accorded the honor of specially close surveillance. Microphones were concealed in offices and living quarters. In their inquisitorial zeal the military people exceeded their official instructions and often followed a policy of their own, without reference to Washington. General Groves was to boast—later—of having done everything in his power to hinder cooperation with the British.

Oppenheimer's participation in the nuclear weapon project officially began in 1942, at the Metallurgical Laboratory of Chicago, which at that time was the main center of uranium fission research in the United States. He had had to fill in a questionnaire, in which he admitted having belonged to left-wing organizations. He was aware that in the eyes of the security services membership in such organizations rendered a man ineligible for work of high national importance. Whatever White House policy might be, many officials of those services made no secret of the fact that they regarded America's entry into the war against the Axis as only the tactical preliminary to a longer struggle, in which the ultimate enemy would be the Soviet Union. Anyone suspected of sympathy toward the Soviets, or even of being likely to disapprove of America's eventual attack on her temporary "ally", must be excluded in advance from any key post in the conduct of the war. This precaution applied particularly to scientists; their work put them in possession of important secrets, which it was thought they might be tempted to communicate to their Soviet colleagues.

Oppenheimer, however, had answered the questionnaire without much apprehension. Three years earlier he had severed all connection with his former political friends; so had his wife, who had frequented the same circles in times gone by.

But in June 1943 he received an urgent call from his former fiancée, the Communist student of psychiatry; he went to see her in San Francisco and stayed till the next day. This was not the first such meeting they had had since his marriage. But on this occasion he warned his friend that he would not be seeing her again for a long time, maybe several years; he had accepted an assignment which he could not talk to her about and which necessitated his leaving Berkeley; he was not allowed to say where he would be living.

Oppenheimer did not suspect that the security sleuths were following all his movements, and that a lengthy report on his journey to San Francisco and his relations with a militant left-winger had been sent to the War Department in Washington. The impact of this report was felt by General Groves in mid-July, in the form of a note stating that, for security reasons, it was impossible to confirm the appointment of J. Robert Oppenheimer as director of the Los Alamos laboratory. The General immediately sent for Oppenheimer, received his direct assurance that he had long since broken off relations with the Communists, and decided to ignore the ban.

The General had no sympathy with Communism himself, and was unfavorably disposed toward the Russian-American alliance. But he needed Oppenheimer. The Los Alamos laboratory was going through a difficult time because of the poor living conditions of the scientists in the residential barracks erected on the plateau; only Oppenheimer was capable of keeping up everyone's morale and maintaining the general enthusiasm of the first few weeks. Discouragement would become deeper if he left, and the team which he'd assembled with such difficulty would be in danger of disintegrating. Using the special powers conferred on him at the inception of the Manhattan Project, General Groves requested that the security report on Oppenheimer be shelved; this was granted, and Oppenheimer's appointment confirmed.

The General's brusque military exterior concealed a certain shrewdness, enabling him to foresee the psychological consequences of his decision. In relation to General Groves Oppenheimer had ceased to be a free man. The scientist was not only grateful for this timely intervention on his behalf; he also realized that a sword of Damocles was now hanging over his head and that only the hand of General Groves prevented it from descending. At any moment his political past might rise up against him and rob him of his assignment to build the bomb.

Oppenheimer's false step. Whether because he wanted to prove to himself that he had abjured his past, or whether because he wanted to prove it to the Army authorities, Oppenheimer committed a strange error. At the end of August, happening to be in Berkeley, he visited a security agent there and told him that the Russians had been trying for some time to get information about the Manhattan Project. An Englishman named Eltenton, who had lived for some years in the U.S.S.R., had asked a third party to get into touch with some of the scientists working on the project. Oppenheimer was unwilling to name the intermediary, who, he implied, had acted in good faith.

This fiction was not completely ungrounded in fact. Its origin was a conversation which had taken place several months previously between Oppenheimer and a friend of his, Haakon Chevalier. The son of a Scandinavian mother and a French father, Haakon Chevalier was a teacher of Romance languages at the University of California. He and Oppenheimer got on well together, and their friendship enabled the physicist to renew his contact with the atmosphere of distant Europe, its literature and philosophy. But on that particular day their conversation touched at one point on a more concrete subject. Let us quote from Jungk, who has collected direct oral evidence. The two were in the kitchen of the Oppenheimers' house at Berkeley; their wives were talking together in the living-room:

" 'Oppie' began to mix Martinis. His friend proceeded to inform him that he had recently been talking to a man they both knew named George Eltenton. The latter had complained to him that in spite of the fact the American and Soviet Governments were allied no interchanges of new scientific information took place between the scientists of the two countries. He went on to ask Chevalier whether it would not be possible to persuade Oppenheimer to pass on scientific data in a private capacity. Oppenheimer reacted to Eltenton's suggestion in the manner Chevalier had foreseen.

"So far as the latter remembers Oppenheimer exclaimed: 'That's not the way to do these things!' According to Oppenheimer's own subsequent statement his answer was even more pointed. He believed he had retorted: 'That would be a frightful thing to do!' and 'But that would be high treason!' "

Oppenheimer's reaction is an indication of the distance he had traveled in a few years. To appreciate this, we must forget the state of cold war in which we live today and re-

J. R. Oppenheimer

Examining the wreckage of the scaffolding on which the first atom bomb was tested in 1945

Oppenheimer's house at Princeton

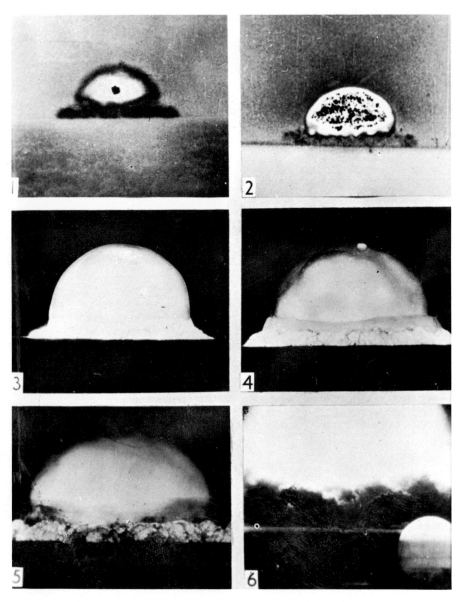

The first atom bomb explosion
New Mexico, July 1945

On television with Senator Brian MacMahon, Mrs. Roosevelt
and David Lilienthal, 1950

Oppenheimer with Professor Jules Perez, dean of the Faculté des Sciences in the
University of Paris, before a lecture at the Sorbonne, 1958

With Professor C. J. Bakker, director of C.E.R.N. (Centre européen de Recherches nucléaires), Zurich, 1958

member the atmosphere of the winter of 1942–43, the time of Stalingrad and the Allied landing in North Africa. Roosevelt was enthusiastically lauding the struggle of the United Nations against Nazism, and Hollywood had begun turning out pro-Soviet films.

No doubt there was never any question of sharing military secrets with Moscow. But in reacting so violently against the idea of transmitting scientific results to Soviet colleagues, when scientists of all countries had communicated so freely with each other before the war, Oppenheimer was displaying something more than a willingness to conform with official policy; he was voluntarily identifying himself with the most reactionary views of big business and the Army, which were not, as yet, those of Washington. It is one thing for an intellectual to accept war-time discipline as a matter of necessity, and another thing to raise it to the level of a moral principle.

Oppenheimer thought that by denouncing Eltenton's feeler as a piece of espionage he was confirming his own loyalty in the eyes of the security people. In fact, however, he was placing a terrible weapon in the hands of those same people, who had never stopped suspecting him and who begrudged his having been kept at the head of the Los Alamos laboratory against their wishes. It was not long before he was sent for by Colonel Pash, the man who had signed the report demanding his dismissal. Verbatim records of this and subsequent interrogations were published long afterward. There is something pathetic and moving in these cat-and-mouse dialogues in which a scientist of stature, a man of superior intelligence, can be watched struggling against the insidious questions of a military policeman, and trying in vain to escape from a trap of his own making.

Oppenheimer had put himself into the position of having to maintain a lie and to withhold genuine information. The lie—or, at least, the distortion of facts—consisted of his having asserted that several participants in the Manhattan Project had been informed of Eltenton's move, when in fact the only one to have been so informed was himself. The information which he at first would not give was the name of his friend Chevalier; this refusal was unacceptable to the security people and confirmed them in their opinion of him.

Here is a characteristic extract from the first interrogation: [1]

Pash: Here's the thing—we of course assume that the people who bring this information to you are 100 per cent with you and therefore there is no question about their intentions. However, if—

Oppenheimer: Well, I'll tell you one thing—I have known two or three cases, and I think two of the men were with me at Los Alamos—they are men who are very closely associated with me.

Pash: Have they told you that either they thought they were contacted for that purpose or that they were actually contacted for that purpose?

Oppenheimer: They told me they were contacted for that purpose.

Pash: For that purpose.

Oppenheimer: That is, let me give you the background. The background was—well, you know how difficult it is with the relations between these two allies, and there are a lot of people who don't feel very friendly with Russia, so that the information—a lot of our secret information, our radar and so on, doesn't get to them, and they are battling for their lives and they would like to have an idea of what is going on and this is just to make up, in other words, for the defects of our official communication. That is the form in which it was presented.

Pash: Oh, I see.

After a few more feints of this sort, the Colonel naturally returned to the thing he wanted to know—the intermediary's name.

Pash: Well, now I may be getting back to a little systematic picture. . . . These people whom you mentioned, two are down there with you now. Were they contacted by El-tenton direct?

Oppenheimer: No.

Pash: Through another party?

Oppenheimer: Yes.

Pash: Well, now, could we know through whom that contact was made?

[1] Quoted here from Jungk, pp. 146–7. [Tr.]

Oppenheimer: I think it would be a mistake, that is, I think I have told you where the initiative came from and that the other things were almost purely accident and that it would involve people who ought not to be involved in this.

Oppenheimer had let his hand get caught in the machine; from now on, the counterespionage robots never let him go. He was called to Washington, where he refused several times to reveal the name of Haakon Chevalier but showed no great resistance to the pressure brought on him to indicate which individuals among his friends and acquaintances he suspected of being Communists. Witch-hunting has a remorseless logic. From the moment when Oppenheimer had decided of his own free will to approach the security people with information, he became part of the system and could find no reason for not denouncing individuals who, by definition, were suspect. With regard to the famous intermediary, whom he alleged to have contacted "several" of the participants in the Manhattan Project, he did his best by affirming that the man had no evil intentions and consequently ought not to be mixed up in the affair. But the net was tightening. In the Oppenheimer dossier, which never left Colonel Pash's desk, was the following note, sent in by a security agent in September 1943: "It is considered that Oppenheimer is deeply concerned with gaining a worldwide reputation as a scientist and a place in history as a result of the D.S.M. project. It is also believed that the Army is in the position of being able to allow him to do so or to destroy his name, reputation and career, if it should choose to do so. Such a possibility, if strongly presented to him, would possibly give him a different view of his position with respect to the Army. . . ."

More than one view is possible concerning the psychological truth of such an assessment. But it certainly reveals the brutal cynicism with which the politico-military machine was manipulating a preeminent American scientist who had fallen into their hands. When he eventually received a direct order to name the intermediary, Oppenheimer gave in and mentioned Chevalier, who lost his university post as a result and had to go into exile. Chevalier did not find out what had caused his tribulations until much later, when, during another inquiry, Oppenheimer told the whole truth and acknowledged that he had "amplified" the Eltenton affair.

Atomic scientists versus *the bomb.* For the time being, the viselike pressure brought to bear on Oppenheimer by the security authorities was relaxed. Work at Los Alamos was continued strenuously. It had been thought at first that a year would suffice for making the bomb, but this estimate was soon seen to be wrong. Meanwhile the war went on. At Strasburg, in November 1944, the Americans captured a bundle of papers containing information about German work on uranium fission. These papers showed that, contrary to the fear which had acted as both justification and stimulus to the refugee scientists in the United States, the Germans were far from being able to manufacture an atomic bomb. They had no factory for separating uranium 235, no reactor producing plutonium. The nightmare of a Nazi nuclear weapon was dissipated at one stroke, and the outcome of the war was no longer in doubt; the Allied armies were already penetrating into Germany.

Then the idea began arising among the atomic physicists that the bomb was no longer needed, and that humanity could be spared the apocalypse which they had been preparing for it.

Nevertheless there were not many who urged immediate cessation of work on the bomb. Such a sweeping act of renunciation, at the very moment when success was in sight, did not come easily to men who for many months had given of their best to bring the project to realization. Nor were they deaf to the argument, much canvassed by the military, that Japan was still to be vanquished and that American possession of the bomb would save large numbers of American lives by shortening the struggle on the various Pacific fronts. And so, in their moral simplicity, they began accepting the idea that in order never to have to use the new weapon it would be enough to let its power be seen by the eyes of the world. After that, agreement between the victorious great powers would remove the threat forever and make it possible to use uranium fission for peaceful ends alone.

The scientists did not know that, in any case, Japan had virtually lost the war already. And above all they did not know that the struggle against fascism was not the heart of Washington's policy, or at least would soon cease to be so;

that the bomb, though it might fall on Japan, was a weapon of intimidation for ensuring American supremacy after the war and, in this sense, was really aimed at the Soviet Union. These sorcerer's apprentices applied their energies piecemeal, at first in an effort to circumscribe the mischief of the devil they themselves had conjured up, and later in the forlorn hope of persuading it back into its bottle. But the military men knew what they wanted; so did Oppenheimer, the chief sorcerer, who was not afraid of his devil but, on the contrary, wanted to see its hideous power fully deployed.

Already in August 1944, Niels Bohr had presented to President Roosevelt a memorandum uttering a warning against "the terrifying prospect of a future competition between nations about a weapon of such formidable character." He suggested that the only country which was on the brink of possessing such a weapon should, without delay, take the initiative in seeking such international agreement as would prevent a nuclear armaments race from arising among the future victors. He believed that "personal connections between scientists of different nations might . . . offer means of establishing preliminary and unofficial contact."

In December 1944 Alexander Sachs, one of the President's personal advisers, who had helped Einstein and Szilard five years previously, when they wanted to warn the President of the possibility of a nuclear bomb, succeeded in securing Roosevelt's attention to a plan for considering, immediately after the success of the first experimental explosion, the following courses of action:

(*a*) Demonstration before a delegation of allied and neutral scientists of international standing, and of representatives of all the great religions (including Mohammedans and Buddhists).

(*b*) A report on the nature and implications of the atomic weapon, to be drawn up by the scientists and other representative figures.

(*c*) A warning to be issued thereafter, by the United States and its allies in the Project, to their major enemies in the war, Germany and Japan, that a certain zone would be subjected to atomic bombardment after the expiry of a predetermined time limit, so as to allow for the prior evacuation of human and animal life.

(*d*) Following this demonstration of the effectiveness of

atomic bombardment, an ultimatum to be issued demanding immediate surrender by the enemy countries.

In spring 1945, by a curious irony of fate, the two men who had done most to bring about the construction of the bomb by the United States, Einstein and Szilard, made another approach to Roosevelt, this time in the hope of arresting the course of events. "During 1943 and part of 1944," Szilard later recorded, "our greatest worry was the possibility that Germany would perfect an atomic bomb before the invasion of Europe. . . . In 1945, when we ceased worrying about what the Germans might do to us, we began to worry about what the Government of the United States might do to other countries."

Einstein stressed the need to prevent a nuclear arms race; while Szilard put the emphasis on the idea that, in the situation which had been reached in world affairs, more disadvantages than advantages would accrue to America if she made use of the bomb. Roosevelt died before these two documents reached him; and, even had he read them, they would probably not have made much difference.

For in the meantime at Los Alamos a study group, one of whose members was Oppenheimer, had been set up to choose objectives for atomic bombing. Requirements were as follows:

(1) Target areas should include a high proportion of wooden and other buildings susceptible of the severest damage from blast and from the fire which would follow.

(2) Since the area of devastation was estimated to have a radius of about one mile, a place must be chosen which contained buildings over such an area.

(3) The objectives chosen must be of high military and strategic importance.

(4) The first objective must not have been previously subjected to ordinary bombing, so that the effects of an atomic bomb would be clearly discernible.

In plain language this meant that the objective would be a city—no military installation presented a built-up area of three or four square miles. After the submission of this report four cities, one of which was Hiroshima, were carefully left untouched by the American bombers pounding Japan.

Roosevelt died before making any decision either on the

use of the first atomic bombs, or on international control of nuclear energy. On May 31st, 1945, just after Germany's capitulation, a group called the Interim Committee was set up to advise President Truman. It consisted of five political representatives and three scientists engaged in military research. Four atomic specialists were added to it: J. R. Oppenheimer, Enrico Fermi, Arthur H. Compton and Ernest O. Lawrence. General Groves also attended its meetings. The four atomic physicists found that they were being asked not whether, but how, the bomb should be used. And the committee's conclusions were that it should be used against Japan as soon as possible, that it should be dropped on a military installation situated in or near a district covered with dwelling-houses or other highly vulnerable buildings, and that it should be used without prior warning of its nature to the enemy.

The opposition of atomic scientists to the bomb now took the form of an open counteroffensive. The movement started at the University of Chicago, where throughout the war the experts of the Metallurgical Laboratory had tended to orientate their research toward the industrial use of nuclear energy rather than its military applications. The University appointed a committee of seven men, under the chairmanship of James Franck, a Nobel Prize winner and former professor at Göttingen; among its members were Szilard and the biochemist Rabinovitch. In the report which they formally submitted to the Secretary of State for War, the seven spoke not only for themselves but on behalf of all those who had worked on the Manhattan Project. They began by pointing out that scientists had formerly been entitled to disclaim responsibility for the uses to which mankind had put their discoveries. "We feel compelled to take a more active stand now because the success which we have achieved in the development of nuclear power is fraught with infinitely greater dangers than were all the inventions of the past. All of us, familiar with the present state of nucleonics, live with the vision before our eyes of sudden destruction visited on our own country, of a Pearl Harbor disaster repeated in thousand-fold magnification in every one of our own cities."

The signatories warned the United States Government against the illusion that it would hold a monopoly of nuclear power for much longer. They recalled the important work done by British, French, German and Soviet scientists. Even if the processes used in the Manhattan Project were kept secret, the U.S.S.R. would need only a few years in which to catch up. And if a deadly race for nuclear supremacy began, the United States would be at a disadvantage because their high degree of urban and industrial concentration rendered them more vulnerable. The interests of the nation lay either in concluding an international agreement for the abolition of nuclear weapons, or, at the least, in doing nothing which might hasten the manufacture of such weapons by other countries.

And the Franck Report concluded: "We believe that these considerations make the use of nuclear bombs for an early unannounced attack against Japan inadvisable. If the United States were to be the first to release this new means of indiscriminate destruction upon mankind, she would sacrifice public support throughout the world, precipitate the race for armaments and prejudice the possibility of reaching an international agreement on the future control of such weapons.

"Much more favorable conditions for the eventual achievement of such an agreement could be created if nuclear bombs were first revealed to the world by a demonstration in an appropriately selected uninhabited area.

"In case chances for the establishment of an effective international control of nuclear weapons should have to be considered slight at the present time, then not only the use of these weapons against Japan, but even their early demonstration, may be contrary to the interests of this country. A postponement of such a demonstration will have in this case the advantage of delaying the beginning of the nuclear armaments race as long as possible.

"If the Government should decide in favor of an early demonstration of nuclear weapons, it will then have the possibility of taking into account the public opinion of this country and of the other nations before deciding whether these weapons should be used against Japan. In this way, other nations may assume a share of responsibility for such a fateful decision."

The prestige of the signatories was such that the Department of War could not deal with this document by merely putting it away in a drawer. They submitted it to the four atomic scientists co-opted by the Interim Committee. Although the Committee's discussions have not been published, it seems clear that only Lawrence, and perhaps Fermi to some extent, were shaken by the lucid, moving appeal of the "Seven Men of Chicago." As for Oppenheimer, he later recorded his memories of the matter in these terms:

"We were asked to comment on whether the bomb should be used. I think the reason we were asked for that comment was because a petition had been sent in from a very distinguished and thoughtful group of scientists. 'No, it should not be used.' It would be better for everything that they should not. We didn't know beans about the military situation in Japan. We didn't know whether they could be caused to surrender by other means or whether the invasion was really inevitable. But in back of our minds was the notion that the invasion was inevitable because we had been told that. . . .

"We said that we didn't think that being scientists especially qualified us as to how to answer this question of how the bombs should be used or not; opinion was divided among us as it would be among other people if they knew about it. We thought the two overriding considerations were the saving of lives in the war and the effect of our actions on the stability, on our strength and the stability of the post-war world. We did say that we did not think that exploding one of these things as a firecracker over a desert was likely to be very impressive."

The first nuclear explosion. In effect, the military people had been given the green light. Work at Los Alamos went ahead feverishly in the discomforts of a torrid summer. General Groves had ordered that the first bomb be tried out in mid-July. On the 12th and 13th the components were transported in secret to the vicinity of Alamogordo and hoisted to the top of a steel tower erected in the open desert.

Both Oppenheimer and General Groves felt that these were the most important days in their lives. Would the bomb go off? The calculations said "yes"; but calculations could be wrong. The final stages of the work had been marred by several technical hitches, and though these had been quickly overcome they were a reminder that the unforeseeable might always occur.

At 2 A.M. on July 16th, all those designated to take part in the experiment were at their stations, some ten miles from

"Point Zero." Dance music from loudspeakers filled the air. Bad weather caused the trial to be postponed; then, after consultation with the meteorological experts, H-hour was fixed for 5:30 A.M. At 5:15 everyone put on sunglasses and lay on the ground; all faces were turned away from Point Zero. At 5:30 a white light, far more powerful than the sun at midday, lit up the clouds and mountains. "At that moment," writes Jungk, "everyone forgot what he had intended to do. . . . Oppenheimer was clinging to one of the uprights in the control room. A passage from the *Bhagavad Gita,* the sacred epic of the Hindus, flashed into his mind.

> 'If the radiance of a thousand suns
> were to burst into the sky,
> that would be like
> the splendor of the Mighty One—'

Yet, when the sinister and gigantic cloud rose up in the far distance over Point Zero, he was reminded of another line from the same source:

> 'I am become Death, the shatterer of worlds.'

Sri Krishna, the Exalted One, Lord of the fate of mortals, had uttered the phrase. But Robert Oppenheimer was only a man, into whose hand a mighty, far too mighty, instrument of power had been given."

Despite security precautions the news spread rapidly in scientific circles, where it aroused a tremendous wave of opposition to the use of the bomb, or at least to its unrestricted use against civilians. The Alamogordo experiment had shown that the physicists' calculations were wrong, but wrong in the opposite direction to what Oppenheimer had feared. The power of the device was far greater than had been foreseen. Even the measuring instruments which were furthest from Point Zero had been destroyed. It was clear that the nuclear weapon was an instrument of collective destruction, of general massacre.[2] Szilard sent President

---

[2] It is interesting to recall, at the moment when this book is about to be published, the power of the Alamogordo bomb and of those which were to destroy Hiroshima and Nagasaki: 20 kilotons in each case. The Soviet thermonuclear bomb of October 1961 developed a power of over 50 megatons, which is some 2,500 times greater. [Author's note to the original French edition, 1962.]

Truman a petition signed by sixty-seven scientists; but, like its forerunner, it came to nothing in the hands of Oppenheimer and the three other atomic advisers of the Interim Committee.

It may seem surprising that so many collaborators in the Manhattan Project struggled desperately to prevent it from reaching its logical conclusion. The signatories of the Franck report explained their attitude very clearly: "One may point out that scientists themselves have initiated this 'secret weapon' and it is therefore strange that they should be reluctant to try it out on the enemy as soon as it is available. The answer to this question was given above—the compelling reason for creating this weapon with such speed was our fear that Germany had the technical skill necessary to develop such a weapon and that the German Government had no moral restraints regarding its use."

In July 1945, Hitler was dead and Germany was occupied. There was still Japan. The scientists might feel uncertain about her capacity for resistance in the event of the bomb not being used, but no such uncertainty existed in the minds of the administration in Washington. In Switzerland that April, representatives of the Japanese armed forces had put out feelers with a view to discovering on what conditions the Americans would accept a Japanese surrender. In July, the Mikado himself endeavored through his ambassador in Moscow (the U.S.S.R. not yet being at war with Japan) to initiate negotiations, for which purpose plenary powers were given to Prince Konoye.

There was no doubt that the summer of 1945 would see the collapse of Japan. Agreements concluded between the United States and the U.S.S.R. laid it down that the latter would declare war on Japan before the collapse took place, and that nothing short of unconditional surrender would be accepted from Tokyo by the United Nations. Hence no response was made to the Japanese peace feelers. But, on August 6th, Hiroshima was illuminated by the "sun of death". On the 9th it was Nagasaki's turn. In the view of several historians who have made a study of the documents of the period, the use of the bomb was not only a demonstration of power by the United States at the inception of a new epoch in world politics; it was also, in the short term, an attempt to finish the Far Eastern war before Russia could enter it, and thus to prevent her having any hand in the final settlement in that theater. This, as things turned out, was what Oppenheimer and the whole Manhattan Project team had worked for.

5

The Witch-hunt

THE dropping of the atom bombs and the end of the world war were welcomed as a deliverance by most of the scientists on the Manhattan Project. Their feelings were mixed; their success, which was now public knowledge, made them at once proud and afraid. But events had moved into a larger dimension than that of the tormented individual conscience: the world had tasted the horror of the atomic peril, and this new awareness would perhaps abolish forever the threat of another war. The scientists began growing uneasy when they realized that the Army's guardianship of nuclear research, so far from being relaxed, was closing in more tightly than ever and that every effort was being made to mislead the public and underplay the disaster which had befallen the Japanese cities, especially the magnitude of a new danger, unknown to conventional warfare: radioactivity. General Groves even went so far as to testify before a committee of Congress that radiation provided "a very pleasant way to die." Most of the physicists working at Los Alamos and Oak Ridge, and in Chicago and New York, resolved on a campaign to inform public opinion, remove atomic research from military control, and promote the idea of an international ban on nuclear weapons.

Robert Oppenheimer's state of mind was very different. Hailed by the press as the winner of the war against the Japanese and the creator of the weapon whose very power conferred the benefits of the *pax americana* on the whole free world, Oppenheimer was surrounded by the fame which the military people had judged to be his overriding motive; and he was sad, as a man might be who had scaled the heights and gained a closer view of the future than his fellows. According to the system of values which he had accepted, the enemy was Communist Russia. The civil and military rulers of the United States were convinced of the overwhelming material might of their own country, and imbued with the myth of the inherent weakness of Communist society. They believed it would take the U.S.S.R. several decades to master the secrets of nuclear power; and in the meantime America would probably have destroyed Communism. Oppenheimer could not share their blindness. He was alive to the advanced state of Soviet research—though, as events were to show, he underestimated it. Others, such as Einstein, Szilard, Franck and Urey, were equally alive to it, and argued that as a matter of urgency the whole nuclear question must be laid before world opinion, and an agreement concluded with Russia. Oppenheimer, on the other hand, had written as early as October 1944: "Whatever technical superiority this country may at present possess in dealing with the scientific and technical aspects of the problem of the exploitation of nuclear reactions to produce explosive weapons has resulted from a few years of work which was, to be sure, intensive, but inevitably badly planned. Such superiority can probably only be maintained through continued further development of both the technical and the underlying scientific aspects of the problem. . . . No Government can adequately meet its responsibilities for defense if it rests content with the wartime results of this project."

Whereas most of the physicists involved, and even some of the officials, thought there was nothing left to do but "hand back Los Alamos to the desert foxes," Oppenheimer used his powers of persuasion to convince his colleagues that they ought to go on with their work for some time at least. With many of them he was successful, but a few, who had previously looked up to him like the rest, now began detaching themselves from him; they could feel that something in his character had changed.

Then, in October 1945, to everybody's surprise, he announced that he had resigned as director at Los Alamos in order to return to teaching. The bomb having been successfully made, the super-laboratory no longer had a role to play in Oppenheimer's life; it could be handed over to others. His personality was acquiring an added dimension. He was the respected adviser of politicians and generals, the technocrat of the nuclear age. He was working on the plan for international control of nuclear energy which the United States intended to present to the United Nations, and to this extent he could say to other atomic scientists that his preoccupations were in line with theirs. But his work was stamped with a fatal ambiguity. Instead of proposing the destruction of existing nuclear weapons, banning the construction of any more such weapons, and reinstating complete freedom in the exchange of scientific knowledge, the American plan aimed at establishing United States domination in the control of fissile materials and their military and industrial uses. It thus suited the aims of the business circles with which Oppenheimer had become much connected as a result of the rise in his social standing.

Whatever criticisms can be leveled at Russian obsessions in the Stalin epoch—obsessions which are easy to explain historically—there is no doubt that the kind of control proposed by the Americans could not have been found acceptable by Russia; the climate of international feeling was too unfavorable.

The scientists strove in vain to prevent the detonation of experimental bombs on Bikini Atoll in July 1946. In terms of public opinion they were losing ground daily, and most of them ended by accepting the situation because their research work, and even their university salaries, were subsidized by the Army. Hopes of regaining the right to free inquiry and free communication had vanished. The suffocating pressure of police suspicion was even more onerous than during the war against Germany and Japan. In March 1947 President Truman signed the so-called "Loyalty Order," which called for a careful police investigation into the political and moral reliability of all government officials.

Toward the hydrogen bomb. In August 1949, the study of photographs taken at high altitude from an American bomber brought shattering news to the United States authorities: the U.S.S.R. had set off an atomic bomb. To Oppenheimer this was no surprise; he had foreseen it. *The Bulletin of the Atomic Scientists*, which was campaigning against the armaments race, had been printing on its front page a picture of a watch face with the hands showing eight minutes to midnight. This was now altered to three minutes to midnight.[1]

As for the authorities, they had but one thought: to make a super-bomb as quickly as possible; a hydrogen bomb. The possibility of exploiting the fusion of lightweight nuclei had been definitely proved by a small group of physicists under Oppenheimer, as early as 1942; the one who had shown most interest in the question was Edward Teller, a physicist who had been driven out of Germany by the Nazis' racial policy. As we have seen, the study of the fusion bomb had been put off because practical methods of causing fusion were not available at that time. The fission of heavy nuclei—uranium or plutonium—is brought about by bombardment with neutrons. The fusion of light nuclei requires very high temperatures—several millions of degrees; once it has been started it is continued by the energy of the reaction itself, but it cannot start at all unless the fantastically high initial temperature is attained. In 1942 no means of producing it was known; but such a means existed now—in the form of the uranium bomb. Teller, in the interim, had never abandoned the problem. His relations with Oppenheimer were not of the best; he had disliked working under him and had eventually left Los Alamos. He returned there in 1946 for a conference on the possibility of making a hydrogen bomb and from then onward he waged a campaign for the construction of this cataclysmic weapon, whose power, theoretically

---

[1] This *Bulletin* was founded and published by voluntary effort on the part of a group of atomic scientists at the University of Chicago. " 'To say that the *Bulletin* was founded on a shoestring would be to describe it as overdressed at birth,' one of the editors recalls." But it "exercised from the start an influence on leading American intellectuals which was far in excess of the relatively few copies issued". (Jungk, p. 242.) [Tr.]

unlimited, might exceed that of the Hiroshima bomb several thousand times over; the reason being that fusion, unlike fission, was not governed by any question of critical mass.

Oppenheimer had had his bomb; now Teller was to have one of his own, a much finer one, which he had already started calling his "baby".

Oppenheimer took up no definite stand toward the new project; he neither supported nor opposed it. In 1947 he had become director of the Institute of Advanced Study at Princeton. This, one of the most highly reputed centers of scientific research in the world, is maintained by large private contributions. Scholars from the most various fields—mathematics, physics, political economy, philosophy—spend their time there in research and study, with complete freedom to work in their own way. The room occupied by Oppenheimer, in a handsome building surrounded by majestic trees, was very different from the hastily improvised quarters at Los Alamos, and the background was much more attractive than the New Mexican desert. To reach the house allotted to him as director, in which he lived with his wife and two children (a boy and a girl), he had only to take a five minutes' stroll through pleasant meadows. He was in charge of a scientific community of about one hundred and eighty people, most of whom had a doctorate or an imposing list of other degrees. His mornings were given over to the administrative duties; in the afternoons he went on with his own research. He left these ideal surroundings only when called to Washington by the Atomic Energy Commission, of whose General Advisory Committee he was chairman; or as atomic adviser to the American delegation at Lake Success; or when appealed to by one of the many organizations which his authoritative knowledge always caused to seek his advice when an important decision concerning nuclear energy had to be made.

When consulted about the desirability of making a fusion bomb (or thermonuclear bomb) his immediate reaction was one of reserve, if not actual hostility. Like nearly all other atomic scientists, he was by now terrified of the devastating power of future nuclear weapons, whose radius of destruction would far exceed the size of any military objective and might engulf whole countries. The fate of Western Europe meant more to him than to the Pentagon strategists; he knew well (and emphasized on several occasions) that those countries would run the risk of total annihilation in the event of an atomic war.

In October 1949, the General Advisory Committee was convened under Oppenheimer's chairmanship to examine a project for constructing a thermonuclear bomb, the leading supporters of which were Edward Teller and the banker Lewis Strauss; neither of these two was a member of the Committee.

The Committee unanimously considered that to make a thermonuclear weapon would weaken the moral position of the United States. Two members, one of whom was Fermi, came out categorically against it. They proposed that President Truman publicly renounce the project and request the U.S.S.R. to do the same. The six other members, including Oppenheimer, were less forthright but assumed, for the time being at least, an unfavorable attitude: "We all hope that by one means or another the development of these weapons can be avoided. We are all reluctant to see the United States take the initiative in precipitating this development. We are all agreed that it would be wrong at the present moment to commit ourselves to an all-out effort toward its development. . . ."

The battle lasted a little over three months. Lewis Strauss succeeded in winning over several political and military leaders. On January 31st, 1950, President Truman ordered the Atomic Energy Commission to embark on the making of the hydrogen bomb. Most of the scientists were smitten with consternation. Defying the laws of the country, the administration caused the seizure and destruction of several thousand copies of *The Scientific American,* in which periodical the famous physicist Hans Bethe, an expert on the theory of the fusion of lightweight nuclei, had launched an appeal against the super-bomb.

In June 1950 the Korean War broke out. Taking advantage of that special psychological atmosphere which in France used to be called *l'union sacrée,* Teller prevailed on most of the scientists, and even Bethe himself, to support the hydrogen bomb venture. At first there were considerable theoretical difficulties, and it was thought at one point that the project would be abandoned. The obstacles were overcome at an assembly of the most prominent atomic scientists, held at Princeton under the chairmanship of Oppenheimer. The conclusion reached, thanks to a solution proposed by Teller, was that the first experimental explosion could be staged after a year's work. All friction between the two men had temporarily vanished. "Oppie" had regained the enthusiasm of his Los Alamos days.

Later, when he was asked why he had been opposed to the hydrogen bomb in October 1949, Oppenheimer spoke mainly of the technical difficulties which in his eyes had made the prospects of success remote: "I do not think we want to argue technical questions here and I do not think it is very meaningful for me to speculate as to how we would have responded had the technical picture at that time been more as it was later.

"However, it is my judgment in these things that when you see something that is technically sweet you go ahead and do it and you argue about what to do about it only after you have had your technical success. That is the way it was with the atomic bomb. I do not think anybody opposed making it; there were some debates about what to do with it after it was made. I cannot very well imagine if we had known in late 1949 what we got to know by early 1951 that the tone of our report would have been the same."

No one who runs a critical eye over Oppenheimer's behavior during this period can fail to be struck by its divided, contradictory character. He collaborated on the making of the super-bomb, but at the same time continued working out plans for limiting its use. In November 1951, he submitted to General Eisenhower, then commander-in-chief of the Atlantic forces, a plan restricting the use of nuclear weapons to battlefields alone in the case of war in Europe. These waverings reflected more or less exactly those of most other atomic scientists. They were also characteristic of Oppenheimer's cast of thought; he is always too good at seeing every side of a problem to be able to commit himself wholeheartedly in a single direction. When he was working out the plan for international control of fissile materials, he did it in conformity with the prevailing political mythology: American leadership was fundamentally well disposed and would safeguard democracy and freedom for the world; Communism was an evil which must be contained until such time as it could be eliminated. He was aware that such a premise made it virtually impossible for the American proposals to be accepted, and that they were essentially only a maneuver in the field of international opinion; he nevertheless seems to have been genuinely disappointed and alarmed when they were rejected and the way was left open for the armaments race. In response to an appeal from the prominent scientist Urey, a Nobel Prize winner, Oppenheimer added his voice to those protesting against the execution of Ethel and Julius Rosenberg—not, however, because the charge against them, that of having betrayed the "secret" of the atom bomb, was absurd in the eyes of all scientists, but because in his opinion the sentence, death, was too severe.

Teller, at Los Alamos, chafed as much under the authority of Bradbury, the new director, as he had previously under Oppenheimer's. He accused the physicists there of being still under the influence of Oppenheimer and of preferring to make fission bombs. Eventually, against Oppenheimer's recommendation, he managed to get a new laboratory built for himself not far from Los Alamos. But the hydrogen bomb was already on the point of being tested. Strictly speaking it was not a bomb at all, as it was much too heavy to be loaded in an aircraft. The nuclear explosive employed was the hydrogen isotope with atomic weight 3, which had to be maintained at a very low temperature and therefore required a cumbersome freezing apparatus. The first fusion reaction was effected on the ground, on an atoll in the Pacific, on November 1st, 1952. The rest belongs to the story of the contemporary arms race—a race in the making of weapons of extermination. That story is unfortunately incomplete at the time of writing. Let us return to the story of Oppenheimer.

Oppenheimer before his "judges". His initial lack of enthusiasm about the hydrogen bomb had considerably lowered his prestige in official quarters. In July 1952 he surrendered the chairmanship of the Atomic Energy Commission's General Advisory Committee. After Eisenhower had become President, Oppenheimer almost entirely ceased being consulted by the various official bodies whose adviser he had been for a long time past.

With the development of the cold war, the shadow of suspicion and denunciation hung more heavily than ever over scientific circles. America was entering the dark years of McCarthyism. On December 21st, 1953, shortly after his return from Britain, where he had delivered a brilliant series of lectures for the B.B.C. and had been invested with a doctorate, *honoris causa,* at Oxford, Oppenheimer was summoned urgently to Washington by Lewis Strauss, who had been made Chairman of the Atomic Energy Commission. After a minute or two of commonplace conversation Strauss handed him a letter drafted by General Nichols, the Commission's general manager, who was present at the interview. Here again, it was as if fate had taken a hand: Oppenheimer had seen General Nichols for the first time in 1942, sitting beside General Groves in the railway coach in which the latter had offered Oppenheimer the commanding role in the invention and construction of the first atom bomb.

The document drawn up by Nichols was a list of charges based on all the facts, real or supposed, which the secret service had entered in Oppenheimer's dossier over the past ten years. At the time, the accusations were reported by the Associated Press in the following terms:

(1) Dr. Oppenheimer had been associated with Communists, on a number of occasions at the beginning of the war. He had been the lover of a Communist, and his wife was a former Communist. He had contributed generously to Communist funds from 1940 to April 1942.

(2) He had engaged Communists or ex-Communists to work at Los Alamos.

(3) He had made contradictory depositions to the F.B.I. about his attendances at Communist meetings at the beginning of the war.

(4) Dr. Oppenheimer had rejected a suggestion from some individual declaring himself to be a Communist, that he (Dr. Oppenheimer) should pass scientific information to the U.S.S.R., and he had told that individual that such an action would be treason; but for several months he had failed to report the matter to the security authorities.

(5) He had strongly opposed the hydrogen bomb project in 1949, when he was chairman of the General Advisory Committee of the Atomic Energy Commission. He had continued to campaign against the project even after President Truman's decision ordering the Commission to conduct research with a view to executing the project.

The letter concluded by "raising questions as to your veracity, conduct and even your loyalty."

Nichols did not mention that some time before, on December 3rd, President Eisenhower had ordered the "erection of a blank wall between Oppenheimer and all Government secrets." This decision was the sequel to a letter from the former senior assistant of Senator Brian MacMahon, denouncing Oppenheimer as "probably a Soviet agent in disguise"; the letter had caused the F.B.I.'s dossier on Oppenheimer to be reopened, and in the atmosphere of the witch-hunt such an action was tantamount to starting inquisitorial proceedings. Among the contents of the dossier was a deposition against Oppenheimer made in 1950 by Sylvia Grouch, one of the "converts" from the Communist faith. Oppenheimer had already had to clear himself at the time, in an appearance before the Un-American Activities Committee of the State of California, of the charge of belonging to extreme left-wing organizations.

After Oppenheimer had read Nichols' letter, Lewis Strauss gave him twenty-four hours in which to decide whether he would resign of his own accord from his post as a consultant to the Commission, or whether he would prefer the matter to be handled by a "Loyalty" board.

Oppenheimer chose to face the accusations. The trial—the word is apt enough, though legally speaking the proceedings, conducted by a "Personnel Committee", were merely administrative—opened on April 12th and went on for three weeks, during which time Oppenheimer reached his fiftieth birthday. His three judges were a university president who was also a business man and the owner of a number of newspapers and broadcasting stations; an important industrialist; and a professor of chemistry. The role of public prosecutor was performed by Roger Robb, representing the Atomic Commission. Some forty witnesses, including many scientists, gave evidence; the committee also heard tape recordings of the interrogations undergone by Oppenheimer during the war.

The proceedings took place in closed session, but Oppenheimer's attorney had given the press General Nichols' letter of accusation and a reply written by Oppenheimer, in which the scientist recounted in sober but moving terms the services he had rendered to his country and denied absolutely that he had ever passed confidential information to un-

authorized persons. The case aroused intense interest among
the public, especially in intellectual and scientific circles. After
having disappointed many of his friends by hesitating to
support the stand made by the majority of scientists against
the nuclear armaments race, Oppenheimer was suddenly turning into a living symbol of intelligence at bay, persecuted by
the witch-hunters. No doubt he had formerly shown himself
rather too docile in his relations with the inquisitors. But the
public as yet knew nothing of the Chevalier incident. And
Oppenheimer's very moderation, his tendency always to take
up a position of compromise, acquired a special value as an
illustration of the perils with which McCarthyism was threat-
ening American democracy. No sensible man accepted for
an instant the lunatic idea that Oppenheimer was a Soviet
agent; and if he was accused of having opposed the hydrogen
bomb such an accusation, whether justified or not, could do
nothing but make him popular with millions of people in
America and throughout the world. Consequently Oppenheimer's colleagues, despite the reservations many of them
had about him, were almost unanimously on his side, in-
stinctively demonstrating the solidarity they felt as intellectuals hemmed in by the McCarthy menace. And many ordinary people, who respected him as the man who had given
America the decisive weapon in the Second World War, felt
warmly toward him when they learned that the development
of such apocalyptic means of destruction had inspired in
him the same fears as in themselves.

No doubt because of this movement of opinion, the leaders of the Atomic Energy Commission decided to publish
the complete record of the proceedings, a fat volume of nearly a thousand pages, printed in record time.

As one reads that document it is easy to share the sympathy which was aroused in a large section of the public
for the hitherto slightly inhuman figure of Robert Oppenheimer. Faced by the three men appointed to judge him,
none of whom approached his intellectual level, and, especially, by a violently hostile accuser who continually laid traps
to catch him out, Oppenheimer seems to have deliberately
renounced the eloquence and charm which had formerly enabled him to captivate so many of his fellows. We see him
trying only to tell the truth about himself; he admitted, for

example, that the Chevalier incident was almost entirely a fabrication of his own.[2]

Nor did he conceal his hesitations in connection with the hydrogen bomb. These revelations of weakness and inconsistency make a moving effect. From the depositions of other scientists—only one of whom, Teller, spoke against the accused—there emerged clearly the fact that, as Jungk puts it, "it was not only Robert Oppenheimer's fate which was being discussed in that narrow courtroom. The debate concerned all the new, unsolved problems with which the onset of the atomic age had confronted scientists. It concerned the new part they had to play in society, their uneasiness in a world of mechanized terror and counter-terror which they themselves had helped to create, above all their loss of that deeply rooted set of ethical beliefs out of which all science had formerly grown."

The ridiculous assertions that Oppenheimer had been a Soviet agent were, of course, demolished; this was acknowledged by the board. But the witch-hunting hysteria was at its height, and even the Washington administration went in fear of Senator McCarthy's frenzied attacks. Oppenheimer had formerly been associated with Communists; that was enough. In addition, he had not been 100% in favor of the new weapons of extermination. By two votes to one—that of the chemistry professor—he was declared unsuitable for employment in any post entailing access to military secrets, and his contract as adviser to the Atomic Energy Commission was canceled. His subsequent appeal to the Commission was rejected.

Recent years. The Federation of American Scientists immediately launched a protest against the official ostracism inflicted on a distinguished scientist and citizen, who had long served as confidential adviser in governmental deliberations. The Federation drew attention to the consequences of the accusations made against Oppenheimer concerning his

---

[2] It was from the published account of these proceedings that Haakon Chevalier, who now lives in Paris, first learned the cause of the setbacks he had undergone in the United States. He subsequently wrote a novel, *L'homme qui voulait être Dieu* (The Man Who Wanted To Be God), which, though it remains within the boundaries of fiction, can be regarded as an additional source of information on Oppenheimer.

attitude toward the hydrogen bomb: if, henceforth, a government adviser could incur suspicion because of an opinion in which he had been requested to give in the discharge of his duty, scientists would have to consider whether it was possible for them to continue working for government organizations.

The Administrative Council of the Institute for Advanced Study had not even waited for the outcome of the loyalty board's proceedings before expressing its confidence in Oppenheimer. At a meeting on February 15th, it unanimously confirmed his continued appointment as director of the Institute. Lewis Strauss was a member of the Council; he left the meeting three quarters of an hour before the vote was taken, saying he had a train to catch for Washington.

There then ensued several years of behind-the-scenes activities during the Eisenhower and Kennedy administrations, seeking a feasible way to reverse the indictment and restore Oppenheimer's public honor. The first opening came when Strauss left the Commission in 1958, and in 1961 the Federation of American Scientists paved the way for future action by writing directly to the Commission urging a review of the case.

Despite the Kennedy administration's extreme interest in clearing Oppenheimer, they had hesitated for many months because of concern over hostile political reaction. The decision was finally made to give Oppenheimer the Enrico Fermi award, but to postopone action until after upcoming elections.

The Fermi award—named after the Italian-born scientist who directed the team that achieved the first controlled chain reaction—was authorized by the Atomic Energy Act of 1954 in the provision that the Commission may "upon recommendation of the General Advisory Committee and with the approval of the President, grant an award for any especially meritorious contribution to the development, use or control of atomic energy."

Aside from honoring Oppenheimer for "contributions to theoretical physics as a teacher and originator of ideas, and for leadership of the atomic energy program during critical years," the administration now intended to watch for a clue as to whether they could take further steps to reverse the indictment and "clear the name of a scientist placed under a cloud by a prior administration."

However, the decision to grant the award was received in silence in political circles. Was this tacit approval or a lull before a renewed storm? When, on December 2, 1963, President Johnson personally presented the gold medal and $50,-000 award, ignoring the suggestion that he spare himself political embarrassment, the political controversy obviously was not completely stilled. Noticeably absent at the presentation were Republican members of the Joint Congressional Atomic Energy Committee, and especially Hickenlooper, who "could not in good conscience attend" and failed to see even the scientific justification for the award.

Despite the intent of the presentation—that the Government was in part vindicating his honor—Dr. Oppenheimer was not granted security clearance that would permit him to resume his advisory role to the Government. The AEC felt the initiative should come from him, but he was apparently reluctant to apply lest it subject him to the humiliation and publicity of the inquiry and hearings of a decade before.

Over the years, Oppenheimer's international prestige has steadily increased and has taken on a new and more elevated quality. The man who formerly earned the title of "father of the atomic bomb" has now become the type and symbol of the scientist who strives to understand and accept the fullness of his responsibilities in the modern world. In his articles and lectures he continually comes back to the same theme, the problem of the relationship between science and society.

In 1963 he was still arguing that fundamental scientific knowledge will become public in any case, and the imposition of security rules only makes it more difficult to arrive at truth.

This is the man who accepted the highest honor of the Atomic Energy Commission by saying in his characteristically discreet and somber tone, "I think it just possible that it has taken some charity and some courage for you to make this award today," and then quoted the writing of Thomas Jefferson: ". . . the brotherly spirit of science which unites . . . is not always in evidence."

In addition to his administrative duties at Princeton, Oppenheimer has resumed his own scientific work. He represented the International Atomic Energy Agency at the Conference on High Energies, held at Rochester, N.Y., where he presided over a discussion on high-energy interactions between mesons and nucleons.

Nucleons are particles constituting the nucleus of the atom —protons and neutrons. π-mesons are particles whose mass is intermediate between that of the electron and that of the nucleon: the mass of a π-meson is exactly 273 times that of the electron. The existence of these mesons had been foreseen theoretically by the eminent Japanese physicist Yukawa in 1937, but they were not actually observed till ten years later. Yukawa had started from the idea that the electrostatic forces linking the electron (which is negatively charged) to the proton (positively charged) should be conceived as a continuous exchange of electromagnetic waves, photons, between the electron and the proton. In the same way, the unknown forces binding the nucleons together in the nucleus must be interpreted as a continuous exchange of particles between the nucleons. Yukawa calculated the mass of these particles (which were christened "mesons") by using the methods of quantum field theory, which is the extension of the principles of quantum mechanics to the study of fields of force. He found that the mass of the meson must be about three hundred times that of the electron, a figure very close to that subsequently established by experiment.

The big accelerators of today produce π-mesons (there are other kinds of mesons too, but we shall not discuss them here) by causing nuclei to collide with highly accelerated protons. The beams of π-mesons obtained in this manner are aimed at a target—hydrogen, as a rule—and the way in which they react on the nucleus yields evidence about the structure of the latter. The discussion over which Oppenheimer presided at Rochester was devoted to the latest results reached in this branch of research, which it is hoped will give us a better understanding of what goes on in the innermost depths of matter, inside the atomic nucleus.

Oppenheimer has made numerous journeys abroad to give lectures or take part in philosophical discussions. In 1958 he went to Paris and delivered a course of lectures at the Sorbonne. The French Government awarded him the *Légion d'honneur*. In a column in *Le Figaro*, André George commented as follows on the pictures and news items then appearing in the Parisian press: "It seemed to me, insofar as flashlight pictures can be trusted not to deform or transform a face too drastically, that his expression shows the grueling effects of the last four and a half years, years of acute trial. His gray-blue eyes, which are livelier and more luminous than almost anyone's, now look heavily underlined, and surrounded with wrinkles. His face is gashed by two furrows converging toward the nose. He also appeared to me to express himself more often than formerly in English alone. Yet he knows our language well, speaking it slowly and thoughtfully but not without subtlety, and with a fairly abundant vocabulary. People agree in noticing a certain weariness and sadness about him. Nobility exacts its own price. I am strongly reminded of a fine observation by the Scandinavian novelist, Karin Michaelis: 'What time has done with a man's face tells us, more clearly than anything else can, what that man has done with time.' "

6

The Scientist and Society

How are we to envisage the relations of modern science with culture, and those of the scientist with society? These are the problems to which Oppenheimer repeatedly returns, and it can certainly be said that his own life has illustrated their gravity.

One idea frequently emphasized by him is that the ever-growing abstraction and specialization of scientific knowledge have created a gulf which did not previously exist between the scientist and other men, and even between the scientist and his colleagues working in fields outside his own. Science as such has ceased to be communicable to everybody, especially in matters for which there is no longer a valid language save that of mathematical abstraction. A Newton or a Galileo could make his discoveries comprehensible to his contemporaries; in those epochs any cultivated man who wanted to do so could acquire an accurate notion of the latest triumphs of discovery, and was rewarded for the effort by the enrichment of his own culture. But nobody today, unless he is a physicist himself, can really understand Einstein or

Schrödinger. It is true that a whole army of popularizers are doing their best to present contemporary physical research in terms of ordinary language; but in Oppenheimer's view all such efforts are doomed to failure. He even goes so far as to state explicitly that he has never heard a popular exposition of relativity or quantum theory which had anything to contribute to the layman's culture.

Even if we do not agree with Oppenheimer's pessimism we must at least give him credit for having stated clearly one of the gravest of contemporary problems.

Can science be explained to the public? The first obstacle to the wider diffusion of scientific knowledge is the gap which now exists between what a man learned in his schooldays and what scientists have discovered since that time. Until about the end of the last century, anyone who had been through a university, or even anyone with a good secondary education, could later acquaint himself with the work of the greatest scientists, if he wanted to, without too much difficulty; he could understand their experiments and become familiar with the main lines of their theories. Things are different now. The law of the acceleration of history is at work, in science as elsewhere. On the basis of any ordinary educational curriculum of a few years ago, nobody would be able to understand the latest work on the fundamental particles of matter, or even what happens inside the semi-conducting crystals on which our various electronic gadgets depend. We are faced by a historical phenomenon which can be roughly depicted in quantitative terms, thus: until quite recently, the amount of new information discovered by the sciences in one man's lifetime represented an increase of 10% or 20% over the amount of knowledge he had acquired by the time he left school; today the ratio is several hundred per cent.

Moreover, because the whole amount of existing knowledge has become very much greater, it is no longer possible for any one man to take in all of it or even a very large part of it. We have traveled a long way since the days when a highly gifted man could be at once philosopher, artist, geometer and physician. Knowledge has lost its unity; it is like a mirror which was too large; it has broken, and each fragment reflects the universe in its own way. This is perhaps Oppenheimer's deepest regret, something which fills him with a perpetual inner longing.

And finally, in such disciplines as physics, science has reached such a degree of abstraction that it can no longer be expressed in terms of the concepts and relationships known to common sense. Common sense has been built up, over hundreds of millions of years, on realities perceived through our five senses. The realities being explored today are different in scale: they belong to the macrocosm of the galaxies or the microcosm of the atomic nucleus. It is perfectly easy for us to imagine the planets moving around the sun. But we cannot immediately and intuitively conceive that strange entity, a wave-which-is-also-a-corpuscle; and we have made up our minds only in a purely verbal and superficial manner to the fact that time does not flow uniformly throughout the universe.

We cannot deny that the march of science is less easy to follow than it used to be. And yet it has never exerted such power over the shaping of our lives and prospects as it does now. This widening gulf between inherited knowledge and new discovery, and the frequently alarming power wielded by the scientist, have made it urgently necessary for ordinary people to keep pace with the progress of science; but at the same time they have made it almost impossible for this new knowledge to be adequately conveyed in ordinary terms. Magazines, books and popular articles by specialists in the daily press all bear witness to the interest, sometimes eager, sometimes anxious and nervous, which is excited by the magic-makers in the laboratory. Must this curiosity be left unsatisfied or fobbed off with empty words? Has science really become incommunicable?

Oppenheimer says it has. According to him, science has become the property of small groups of specialists who can share it neither with the masses nor with other groups of specialists.

So he says; and yet he himself has attempted to explain to millions of British radio listeners, not, indeed, the equations of Schrödinger, but some of the subtlest and most difficult of the general consequences of the physics based on those equations. This series of lectures, published under the title *Science and the Common Understanding,* is a genuine piece of popularization which would probably have fulfilled its purpose even more effectively if the author had not declared at the outset that his undertaking was an impossible one. And in 1953, speaking to graduate alumni of the University of Princeton, he found these comforting words to say: "But I believe that the science of today is subtler, richer, more relevant to man's life and more useful to man's dignity than the science which had such a great effect on the age of the enlightenment, had such a great effect, among other things, on the forms and patterns, traditions and hopes—reflected in our Constitution—of human society. Science is not retrograde; and there is no doubt that the quantum mechanics represents a more interesting, more instructive, richer analogy of human life than Newtonian mechanics could conceivably be. There is no doubt that even the theory of relativity, which has been so much vulgarized and so little understood, that even the theory of relativity is a matter which would be of real interest to people at large. There is no doubt that the findings of biology and astronomy and chemistry are discoveries that would enrich our whole culture if they were understood."

And in an address (delivered, it is true, to an audience of journalists) Oppenheimer, in April 1958, went so far as to say: "When I speak to the press I am aware that I am talking to a group of men who have a singularly critical destiny in these rather peculiar times. Those of us whose work it is to preserve old learning, and to find new, look to the press to keep the channels of truth and communication open and to keep men *in some sense united in common knowledge and common humanity*" [italics added here].

Of course we must be careful not to misinterpret this passage. Its purpose is not so much to preach the desirability of spreading scientific knowledge among laymen, as indirectly to allude to the barriers of secrecy which, since the last war, have been erected by governments between the laboratories of different countries. It is this intolerable bar to progress which is here denounced in veiled, general terms. On other occasions, Oppenheimer has objected more outspokenly against this "secrecy", rightly detested by all seekers after truth.

Still, the fact remains that by pointing to the necessity of keeping everyone, scientists included, united to some extent by virtue of shared knowledge, he virtually allows that such

The first operational bomb exploding
Hiroshima, August 5th, 1945

The ruins of Hiroshima after the dropping
of the first operational bomb

With Albert Einstein

Oppenheimer at the Institute of Advanced Study, Princeton, discussing the quantum theory with a group of physicists

296th Anniversary of Harvard University, 1947. *Left to right:* R. Oppenheimer, Secretary of State George Marshall, General Omar Bradley, Dr. Conant, President of the University

Senator Brian MacMahon and Robert Oppenheimer at a hearing of the Congressional Joint Committee on Atomic Energy

Inauguration of the Institute of Nuclear Studies at the Weizman Institute, Israel. *Left to right:* Professor Amos de Shalit, Felix Bloch (Stanford University, California), Niels Bohr (Copenhagen, Nobel Prizewinner), Robert Oppenheimer

an enrichment of our culture is possible. Here again, we may be tempted to convict him of a glaring contradiction. But the matter is subtler than it looks at first. On examining his writings more closely we find that what he really regards as incommunicable is not the properly verified, clearly stated content of existing knowledge, so much as the immediate experience of discovery. This is almost as inexpressible as mystical experience. Oppenheimer experienced at first hand, with great intensity, the period of the quantum revolution; its deep curiosity, its groping uncertainties, and its lightning advances into new and awe-inspiring truth. The student to-day, peacefully making his way through a handbook of theoretical physics, can never recapture the flavor, the human quality, of that unique adventure. Neither by repeating the original experiments, nor by reviewing historically the way the research was conducted and the theories were hammered out, can he re-create the mood of Rutherford on observing for the first time the deflection of alpha particles in collision with matter, or that of Louis de Broglie contemplating a beam of light and conceiving the thought that an electron was at one and the same time a corpuscle and a wave.

But is this peculiar to the pioneer discoveries of contemporary physics? On the contrary, is it not a fact that in all ages the major advances of knowledge have been made in moments of special insight, and constitute a special kind of experience? Archimedes with his shout of *Eureka!,* and Newton perceiving the reality of universal attraction, had the same feelings as Rutherford and de Broglie in our own time. Schoolboys learning the principle of Archimedes or the law of gravitation do not re-live those moments of discovery, any more than undergraduates making their first acquaintance with the foundations of quantum mechanics, now well established, re-live the genesis of modern physics. Man's exploration of nature is a continuing conquest to which we can see no end—Oppenheimer, in this connection, rightly stresses that we can no longer harbor the illusions which flourished in some periods of history. The younger generation colonizes the newly acquired territory, the boundaries have been pushed forward, and it is not given to everybody to fight in the front line.

It remains to inquire whether it is true, as Oppenheimer contends, that scientific knowledge has reached such a degree of abstraction and diversity that it can no longer be conveyed to non-specialists. This impression too may be partly caused by an optical illusion distorting our historical perspective. Contemporary physics demands from the individual a conceptual revolution, a dizzy reversal of ordinary ways of thinking about the world. But, on consideration, this does not turn out to be new either. One of our most deeply rooted conceptions is the distinction between *up* and *down,* or *top* and *bottom.* A long struggle, several centuries long, had to be waged before people could see that this distinction was valid only within the framework of our own localized experience, and that what was "up here" to an inhabitant of the Antipodes was "down there" to us. Yet nowadays this is obvious to a child of six. The idea that the earth is not the center of the universe demanded an equally great change in mental habits. There is no doubt at all that many ideas which are now hard to understand, and still harder to explain, will have become common property among our grandchildren.

In a debate on popular scientific exposition, organized by the Association of French Scientific Writers, M. Pierre Auger recalled the fact that scientists themselves often had to make strenuous efforts in order to grasp the new abstractions. In this context he quoted the ruefulness with which Max Planck used to observe his colleagues struggling to understand the intricacies of quantum theory. Planck remarked, with a touch of sardonic humor: "I have come to think that when one has reached a certain age, however learned one may be, there are certain ideas which are too difficult; one may make use of them, but without understanding them very thoroughly. Fortunately, however, people die; so that, after a time, all who could not understand those ideas have disappeared from circulation, and affairs are taken over by those who come after."

It is a remarkable fact that, not infrequently, it is the most outstanding theoretical physicists who show the greatest readiness to address a large lay public. In the United States, for example, there is the Russian-born physicist George Gamow, who has written a large number of popular works; and in France there is Louis de Broglie, several of whose books, if not popular expositions in quite the normal sense of the term, nevertheless exert an appeal far beyond the narrow circle of specialist readers. Frédéric Joliot, in his familiar talks, had no hesitation in trying to render atomic theory intelligible to all his hearers whatever their background. Nor should we forget that the most tireless expositor of the theory of relativity was Einstein himself; leaving his equations on one side, he would produce metaphor after metaphor to convey an intuitive understanding of the identity of inert mass and mass-with-weight, or of the fact that two events which are simultaneous are so only in relation to a single frame of reference.[1]

Where relativity is concerned, M. Auger shows very clearly how people's difficulties in grasping some of its implications are simply the result of preconceived ideas. "Let me, for example," he says, "quote the famous imaginary experiment of the 'Langevin cannon-shell'. I ought to say that, in my experience as a broadcaster on scientific topics, I find that 'Langevin's cannon-shell' is mentioned in one out of every five questions we receive; that is why I quote it here. People are baffled by the Langevin cannon-shell, not because relativity is beyond them, but because they have in their heads a preconceived and very primitive idea: namely, that things are related to one another. In other words, if a traveler gets into the Langevin shell and sets off on a flight, he is still a man, still a part of the same system of relationships as before. Consequently the mode in which he exists must be patterned on the mode in which other men exist. And when you say that the time in terms of which he lives has altered, and that when his journey is over he will have aged less than those who stayed behind on the earth, people find the statement unacceptable—fundamentally so, because the fact that the traveler is a human being is conceived by them as an absolute principle, something beyond any modification; and the public just will not take in what the scientist tells them if it means going outside this principle. I think we ought to start by explaining to them that this preconceived idea is wrong, and that a traveler who has entered the 'Langevin cannon-shell' is no longer a part of humanity, is

[1] *The Evolution of Physics,* by Einstein and Infeld, must be one of the most marvelous expositions ever written in non-mathematical terms for the interested layman. And, incidentally, it gives an admirable description of such matters as that presented in the next paragraph of the text, above. [Tr.]

no longer connected with humanity except through such messages as he receives from us or sends to us; and that there is no direct, absolute communication between one brain and another, one person and another. . . ."

A point too often overlooked—and one on which Oppenheimer does not seem to have commented—is that the controversy as to whether science can be communicated or not is by no means a new one; it did not originate with the science of our own day. Copernicus, in his *Preface* dedicated to Pope Paul III (Paul Farnese), wrote: "Mathematics is written only for mathematicians." On the other hand Gergonne, a mathematician of the last century, declared: "You cannot feel sure that you really understand a theory until you are capable of explaining it in a few words to a passer-by in the street." M. le Lionnais, to whom we are indebted for these quotations, considers the truth to lie between these two extreme positions, and he is no doubt right.

Of all the sciences, mathematics is probably the one which looks the hardest to convey to the layman—not only because it bristles with forbidding symbols, but because it consists entirely of a play of abstractions. Oppenheimer himself admits that he has difficulty in following the developments of modern mathematics. But in recent years a revolution has been getting under way in the teaching of mathematics, with the object of familiarizing small children with such concepts as that of a set or group, which have hitherto been the private domain of specialists. The proponents of this reform believe that it is a simple matter to derive these concepts from the individual's intuitive understanding of his own daily experience, and that his mind will thereafter be much better prepared to understand modern mathematics. This must not be taken as meaning that anyone trained in this way will automatically find it easy to absorb the most recent advances in mathematical thought. But the example does most strikingly make it clear that when people have difficulty in grasping abstractions it is because their mental activity has been patterned in advance on inappropriate lines; and also that all abstractions are grounded in experience. Transposing this view to the realm of physics, we must point out, as we have heard the astrophysicist Schatzman say, that the mathematical formulas used by physicists always correspond directly to physical realities.

These realities belong to a universe which our senses perceive only indirectly, through instruments of detection and measurement. We do not see particles; but we do see the trails of ionization which they make in a cloud chamber, and we can count their impacts in a Geiger counter. They can thus be definitely brought into the world of sense-experience. It is not too fantastic to hope that, some day, the concepts which have found expression in the formulas of wave mechanics will be included in the heritage of common sense, as has happened with the antipodes concept and the heliocentric nature of our planetary system.

It is not without interest to note that Oppenheimer's pessimistic views on the place of scientific research in the life of society seem to have developed in parallel with the crisis he underwent between December 1953 and May 1954, when he was rejected by the state to which he had given power and from which he had received it. The lecture to Princeton alumni, in which he expressed his faith in the human value of science, is dated January 1953. His Reith Lectures for the B.B.C., which contain grave reservations about the possibility of communicating scientific knowledge, were delivered in November and December; it is as if he had sensed the approaching storm. In subsequent writings we find him declaring that science is now the exclusive property of acutely specialized groups and is becoming radically separate from the common culture of mankind. The growing isolation which Oppenheimer attributes to scientists in general is in fact his own, that caused by the crisis in his own life. But this dramatic isolation is not inherent in modern science as such but, rather, in the relationship between the scientist and the authority of the state. This aspect we shall discuss in due course.

The principles of correspondence and complementarity. The fascination exerted by Oppenheimer on other people, especially his pupils, is not only a matter of psychological imponderables. It comes from his cast of mind; he has an original, and sometimes at first bewildering, approach to the problems posed by contemporary developments in science; he displays them in a new light, resolves difficulties, elucidates troublesome hidden contradictions, and makes everything become orderly and obvious. Someone has even said that Oppenheimer possesses "intellectual sex-appeal"; meaning that he induces a kind of euphoria, an intellectual exaltation, in his listeners. There are many great scientists who do not possess this power; their expositions are abrupt and cannot be followed without strenuous effort. And when such men do come down to the layman's level they give the impression of evading the difficulties by oversimplifying them. Oppenheimer relieves our intellectual tensions; he sweeps us along with him in his darting, penetrating perceptions which embrace and dominate a world—the world of contemporary physics—where our minds would otherwise be ill at ease, like a traveler in some overwhelmingly strange country.

An example is the way in which he illustrates the principles of correspondence and complementarity.

The theory of relativity had caused a profound intellectual disturbance by undermining the familiar concepts of absolute space and absolute time. The shock became greater when atomic physicists discovered that their knowledge of a system never permitted them to predict in detail the future behavior of that system. Consider a single atom of a radioactive substance: it may disintegrate under our eyes, while a neighboring and perfectly similar atom may not disintegrate for another ten thousand years. All we can predict is the degree of probability which exists that any such atom will disintegrate within a given time. In the case of a large number of atoms we can show that half of them will have disintegrated after n years; and that half of the remainder will have disintegrated after another period of n years. If the number of atoms concerned is large enough, as it is in the case of any fragment of metal, the law will always work out exactly. It can be predicted that, of any appreciable quantity of thallium 207, one-half will be transformed into lead at the end of 4.8 months. Moreover, the theory enables us to calculate in advance this half-period in the case of any radioactive element, provided we know the composition of its nucleus. But if, instead of considering the piece of thallium as a whole, we ask ourselves about one of its atoms individually, no prediction whatsoever can be made. It may turn into lead instantaneously or after a thousand centuries. Nuclear physics cannot offer us certainty here; only a probability. And, we repeat, the atom which disintegrates now and the one which does so after a thousand centuries are subject to the same conditions; there is no cause with which we can connect the difference between the fate of one and the fate of the other. This also applies to electrons passing from one level (or state) of energy to another. When a large number of atoms are excited (for example, by radiation) some of the electrons are brought into more or less unstable states of higher energy; each of these electrons returns to its former state by emitting a photon. But they do not all undergo this transition at the same instant; and there is no way of foretelling when the transition will occur in any one atom. Yet there is no cause acting on one rather than another.

So, after shattering our ideas of space and time, science had proceeded to ruin what was to all appearances its own foundation, the very condition of all logical thought: the principle of causality. Identical situations, determined by identical causes, can produce different outcomes. "How could all this be," wrote Oppenheimer, "and yet leave the largely familiar world intact as we knew it? Large bodies are, of course, made up of atoms. How could causality for bullets and machines and planets come out of acausal atomic behavior? How could trajectories, orbits, velocities, accelerations, and positions re-emerge from this strange talk of states, transitions, and probabilities? For what was true yesterday would be true still, and new knowledge could not make old knowledge false. Is there a possible unity between the two worlds and what is its nature?"

The contradiction vanishes when we remember that the new physics had its point of departure in the discovery of the quantum of action. When action takes place on quantum scale, as is the case in the atomic world, the laws of physics are statistical; they express probabilities. "Where actions are large compared to the quantum of action, the classical laws of Newton and Maxwell will hold." In practice, this means that in any order of phenomena whose masses and distances are large compared with those of elementary particles, the acausal characteristics of atomic phenomena become negligible; statistical laws then lead to probabilities which amount to certainties.

Oppenheimer does not confine himself to showing how this "principle of correspondence" between the laws of the atomic world and those of the macroscopic universe opened up the road which led to the development of wave mechanics. He underlines the philosophical and even social significance of the principle. New discoveries do not cancel previous knowledge; the latter remains valid in its own various domains. Any discovery, no matter how revolutionary it may be, leaves intact an immense world of fact whose reality has been definitively established. "This is one reason why, however great the novelty or scope of new discovery, we neither can, nor need, rebuild the house of the mind very rapidly. This is one reason why science, for all its revolutions, is conservative. This is why we will have to accept the fact that no one of us really will ever know very much. This is why we shall have to find comfort in the fact that, taken together, we know more and more."

Thoughts like these have a debunking effect on the excesses committed by some popular expositors of science. There is a certain public which is greedy for philosophical thrills; it likes to burn its wings at the delusive lights set up by these seers. Some new discovery or theory is asserted to have stultified all that went before it; but this in itself throws suspicion on the new contribution, since there is no reason why it should not be stultified in its turn by some other sensational novelty.

Oppenheimer, as we have noted already, makes short work of those would-be philosophers who triumphantly discovered a proof of free will in Heisenberg's uncertainty principle, and in the fact that quantum mechanics shows the impossibility of predicting the individual behavior of an elementary particle. They say this proves that non-causality is the very essence of nature, and that man is free. But even if we allow this unjustifiable extrapolation from the scientific to the moral or metaphysical realm, the reasoning still falls to the ground; and the principle of correspondence is what makes it do so. The human brain is made up of billions of billions of atoms, and the tiniest psychological event involves so many of them that, considered from the physico-chemical aspect alone, it must result from a definite causation and not a probability. If we are unable to make absolutely sure predictions in this realm, the reason is that we are still a long way from understanding all the workings of our bodies and that the number of factors at work in any one case is so enormously large that we cannot conceivably be aware of all of them. This practical impossibility is of quite a different nature from the intrinsic impossibility, in quantum mechanics, of predicting the behavior of an individual electron, or of measuring, exactly and simultaneously, its movement and its position.

By trying to place such a question on a scientific footing, the thinkers in question risk giving the game away to the very adversaries they seek to confound, namely certain nineteenth-century materialists who, by a confusion similar to that of the metaphysicians, invoked causality in order to refute the reality of freedom. But free will—whatever our conception of it may be—is not something on the same plane as physical phenomena. An act of will has nothing in common with the fact that an electron passes indifferently through one hole in a screen or through a neighboring hole, at least unless we credit the electron with possessing intelligence and moral sensibility! And in order to push to its logical conclusion this attempt to resolve religious and moral problems by means of analogies with wave mechanics, we should have to admit that human beings, like electrons, could be mistaken for one another and cease to be individually identifiable. Which would be a curious argument for the existence of moral responsibility!

A sudden touch of mysticism, it is true, is to be found here and there in Oppenheimer's thinking; the fact that his thought is so far removed from a poverty-stricken mechanistic determinism gives all the more weight to his disdainful condemnation of tuppeny-ha'penny metaphysics. But his mysticism is not of the kind which likes to dwell on the pathos of human destiny, in preference to cultivating a rational understanding of the universe.

Another example of the depth of his thinking is to be found in his comments on the principle of complementarity.

As we have seen already, an electron can be regarded either as a continuously propagated wave presenting phenomena of interference like those of light waves, or as a definitive, localized particle. According to circumstances, either its energy or its position can be defined and measured; but the fact that one of these measurements is undertaken precludes any possibility of undertaking the other. Physicists say that a particle's energy and position are connected by a relationship of complementarity.

Here again, Oppenheimer convicts of superficiality those

who, arguing by analogy, declare that psychological processes cannot be apprehended as they are, because they are modified by the act of our observing them. "It is, of course, not the fact that observation may change the state of an atomic system that gives rise to the need for a complementary description; it is the fact that, if the observation is to be meaningful, it will preclude any analysis or control of that change that is decisive."

Nevertheless, as a mode of thinking, an attitude of the human mind confronted with the world, complementarity holds good in some domains far removed from atomic physics. It is decidedly earlier than atomic physics, as we can see from the example of biology. So far, it has not proved possible at once to observe a living cell and to make a physico-chemical study of its constituents. It is true, however, that the obstacles to doing so seem likely to be overcome.

One of our deeper needs is to give a complementary description of the various aspects of our own lives: intelligence and emotion, introspection and action, the practice of an art and the description of that practice. This applies also to "the great antinomies that through the ages have organized and yet disunited man's experience": the frail and transitory character of earthly things, and the fact that every event has its place and its consequences in eternity; growth and order; causality and finality. Each of these modes of apprehending life is legitimate in its own way, but each excludes the other.

Finally, Oppenheimer extends the notion of complementarity to the antithesis between the individual and society, and to that between the scientist and society. The scientist cannot help being aware that his investigations may bear destructive fruit, but he cannot suspend his work for that reason; investigation is his *raison d'être*. Nor can society demand that he do otherwise; all he need ask himself is whether his work is capable of contributing to human knowledge. There is thus a relation of complementarity between the moral justification of science and the personal motives of the scientist.

There is no denying that at this point Oppenheimer's words are a little less than clear, a little less than strictly logical. The fact is that they bring us close to the heart of his personal dilemma. Is the scientist responsible for what he creates? Were the atomic physicists right to make the bomb which fell on Hiroshima, and are they right to continue serving the authority of the state by providing it with weapons of mass destruction?

7

The Scientist and Authority

VERY few of the physicists who made the bomb have been able to avoid searching their own hearts and pondering on the responsibilities of the scientist in the modern world.

One recalls the gesture of a young Englishwoman, Helen Smith, who was Max Born's assistant. When she heard of the existence of the atomic bomb she abandoned physics for jurisprudence. Perhaps, if we looked, we might find a few other cases of the same kind. But it would be difficult to see in them anything more than a personal escape-route, an individual way of salvation. Those taking that path have kept their consciences clear; they have dealt with their own immediate problem. But the general problem is still there. Nobody abolishes physics and its applications merely by ceasing to be a physicist.

In 1954 Hans Bethe, one of the creators of the thermo-nuclear bomb, voiced his distress: "I am afraid my inner troubles stayed with me and are still with me and I have not resolved this problem. I still fear that maybe I have done the wrong thing. But I have done it."

Einstein never forgave himself for having drawn Roosevelt's attention to the possibility of nuclear weapons: "If I had known," he declared after the war, "that the Germans would not succeed in constructing the atom bomb, I would never have moved a finger."

Oppenheimer has not expressed the same regrets. But in 1956, weary and exhausted, he said: "We did the devil's work." As early as 1947—before personal catastrophe had forced him to revise his views on certain aspects of American democracy—he acknowledged the "profound disturbance and moral anguish" of which many of the physicists who had worked together on the bomb were unable to rid their minds.

The question has often been discussed whether, at any point, the physicists had it in their power to halt the process whose end-result was a weapon of mass destruction. If we look at the story in retrospect, as if watching a film being run through backward, it is easy to discover crucial moments, decisions which could have been differently made and would have profoundly modified the subsequent course of events. Heisenberg has asserted his conviction that if, in 1939, a few physicists had jointly decided that atomic energy was not to be used for military ends, it would not have been so used. Even after the trial explosion at Alamogordo it would still have been possible for the scientists, especially Oppenheimer, to avert the Hiroshima massacre. But Oppenheimer did just the opposite. It is true, that where the hydrogen bomb was concerned, he hesitated; but eventually he came around to the idea, even to the extent of denying later that he had hesitated at all, except on technical grounds. And there is no doubt that, by giving an inaccurate picture of the plans being made in Washington just after the war, he used his position to mislead those of his colleagues who were demanding prompt action against the menace of the arms race.

His attitude was at least consistent. It was in line with the organizing of an air reconnaissance system along the Soviet borders (a system in whose creation he had a hand, after the war), and with the denouncing of physicists suspected of Communism or fellow-traveling. All this makes sense, both logically and morally, provided you accept the official values of American society in the mid-twentieth century. Oppenheimer had rallied to them on coming under the power of General Groves and the security services. The country of Jefferson was the incarnation of good, of progress and democracy; evil had been represented for a time by Hitler, and was now upheld in more lasting fashion by Communism.

How did so subtle a mind as that of Oppenheimer, so quick to see the other side to any and every question, come to accept these simple Manichaean views? Robert Jungk dates Oppenheimer's conversion from the time of General Groves' request to Washington that Oppenheimer be confirmed in his appointment as director at Los Alamos, despite unfavorable security reports: ". . . Robert Oppenheimer had now decided to devote himself to the service of his native land. For the first time he believed that he had both feet on the ground of something real. That reality had been fashioned out of coarse material, no doubt. Rough, simple men like Leslie Groves had the biggest say in it. But they were ready to listen to the advice of a superior mind. Oppenheimer had come down from the rarefied air of the heights. He was no longer just an 'unpractical' and 'rootless' intellectual. He had finally chosen a certain kind of 'complicity'. Now, at last, he 'belonged'."

Perhaps this comfortable feeling of social re-integration had a special attraction for the son of Jewish immigrants, a man who had found that there were intangible obstacles preventing his being fully acceptable to the upper reaches of American society. He had always needed to be part of the group, to be popular. Jungk mentions this ethnic factor as a theme recurring in conversations about the "Oppenheimer case". But we must beware of this line of explanation; it looks promising but leads us nowhere—or astray. After all, Einstein had much stronger reasons for reacting in that way but he never did so; he remained free from any kind of conformism. Instead of tempting us into empty psychological speculation, the life story of "the father of the atomic bomb" should be made to pose for us the general, and extremely real, problem of the scientist's relation to the state, in an era when the destinies of states are so much affected by the work of scientists.

By 1940, this relation had assumed a tragic character in the countries of the Old World, both as regards science itself and as regards the personal safety of many scientific men. In the Germany of Hitler and Goebbels, Marxism, psychoanalysis and quantum physics were condemned wholesale; they were all "Jewish"! German scientists had either to escape from the country or to perform a humiliating ideological kow-tow. *Mutatis mutandis,* the situation did not look much better, on a cursory glance, in the U.S.S.R. Dogmatic Stalinism, that wretched caricature of Marxism, indiscriminately hunted down the heresy of "idealism" in every upsurge of new scientific thought. This persecution did less damage than might have been expected, however, at least in physics, as it did not prevent scientists from pushing ahead with research inside their laboratories in whatever they themselves considered the best way. Despite superficial resemblances, there was an essential difference between the lot of science in the Third Reich and in the state which had developed from the October Revolution. In the U.S.S.R., cultural values held a high place; whatever aberrations authority might perpetrate, the importance of scientific research in the building of a socialist state was never in dispute. Credits and status, and everything necessary for training tomorrow's generation of scientists, were accorded lavishly at all times. But the weight of the chauvinism and spy-mania which were characteristic of the Stalin period fell heavily on those atomic physicists from abroad who had thought to find political refuge, and a chance to continue their work, in the U.S.S.R.

Fritz Houtermans, who had studied at Göttingen and collaborated with Bethe in discovering the thermonuclear processes producing the energy of the sun, and another physicist, Alexander Weissberg, were arrested by the Soviet police and examined on fantastic charges of sabotage and spying. Till the day before his arrest, Houtermans had been doing important work on the absorption of neutrons by nuclei. In 1940, he and Weissberg were taken by the Soviet police to Brest-Litovsk and handed over to the Gestapo. News of their arrests in Russia, and other things of the same kind, had been learned by Western physicists when, in 1938, Niels Bohr had in all good faith sent two of his pupils to the U.S.S.R. to ascertain the possibilities for new refugees from Austria who wished to settle there. Some years later these incidents powerfully reinforced the "democratic" mythology put out by the State Department in Washington: to serve the might of the United States of America, whoever the enemy, was to defend the spirit of freedom, which is as precious to science as bread is to mankind. There were many atomic scientists who did not accept this simple scheme of things. After the German surrender there was more and more heart-searching, more and more open opposition to the development of nuclear weapons. But it must be admitted that the soldiers and politicians had the last word on the whole; scientists in revolt had to fall back into line, as the case of Bethe so eloquently shows. As for Oppenheimer and Teller, they never deviated from the officially approved attitude.

Individual psychological peculiarities; ambition; the feeling that successful scientific or technological work is its own reward ("art for art's sake")—none of these explanations is complete or convincing. Nor can it be said that atomic scientists have merely been doing a job of work, unaware of the moral problem confronting them. They themselves have admitted the contrary. The truth is simpler. There is no reason to doubt the deep sincerity of Robert Oppenheimer in repeatedly stressing, in his writings during the post-war years, the basic antagonism between science and the spirit of authority, and the necessity of safeguarding the values of a free and liberal civilization—the alternative being an age of darkness, an eclipse of progress. His passages on this theme are forceful and impressive, and no doubt everybody who is concerned for the life of the mind would whole-heartedly subscribe to them. But the question of the type of society best suited to foster and develop those values, remaining faithful to them amid all the shifting pressures of contingency—that is another matter. Oppenheimer settles it after a fashion; an arbitrary, irrational fashion, as he himself involuntarily admits; for what he asserts (has, indeed, asserted several times) is that political problems cannot be solved by the methods of scientific thought.

Science and the spirit of freedom. We shall attempt no general discussion of this subject here; we shall simply point to the eloquence and conviction with which the author of *The Open Mind* shows that the professional practice of scientific research encourages intellectual and moral qualities which could be equally useful in other fields as well. The first of these qualities is a complete absence of the spirit of authority. As we have pointed out, this does not mean in the least that confirmed and accepted truths are forever being called in question; on the contrary, science is conservative and advances by transcending the knowledge already acquired, not by superseding it. But in research, on the battle front where new knowledge is won, the possibility of error has at all times to be reckoned with; indeed, the refinement of techniques for detecting errors is at once the condition and the criterion of progress. To refrain from dogmatizing, to remain modest in one's attitude to the complexities of nature, to be cautious in one's statements—all these are implicit necessities of scientific research. "The scientist is free to ask any question, to doubt any assertion, to seek for any evidence, to correct any error. Where science has been used in the past to erect a new dogmatism, that dogmatism has found itself incompatible with the progress of science; and in the end, the dogma has yielded, or science and freedom have perished together."

Thus there is a kind of pre-established harmony between scientific research and the democratic ideology of the country which produced the "Declaration of Rights." Research prospers all the more for being surrounded by the climate of freedom which is natural to it, and, reciprocally, the spirit which animates science reinforces the structures of a free society.

To the virtues of guarded utterance and freedom from dogmatism, modern science adds that of constant cooperation, the habit of collective effort. The scientist is a member of a harmonious community; the very nature of his daily life and work gives him a certain species of wisdom and serenity; a certain moral stamp, in fact. An important aspect of the relationship between the scientist and society is the necessity for ensuring that mankind as a whole shall benefit from the human values proper to the scientific atmosphere. This, in fact, is the contribution owed by contemporary science to culture and progress. It is not an easy thing to bring about, and as we follow the curve of Oppenheimer's thinking we are not surprised to see him having doubts about the communicability of science. For what needs to be communicated is not the substance of the knowledge acquired but the experience of its acquisition; and that experience belongs exclusively to those who have undergone it. There is a radical difference between the process of discovery and the dissemination of its results through university teaching. No artifice of educational technique can bridge the gulf. A laboratory experiment which a professor sets up for a student, knowing in advance what the result will be, is a totally different thing from the same experiment performed for the first time, in a groping attempt to wrest a new secret from nature. Even wider is the gulf between original discovery and the popular exposition of science for the benefit of the general public. Such is the conclusion we can reach for ourselves but which Oppenheimer avoids for reasons of literary convenience. It nevertheless follows from his own premises, namely that in the modern world the scientist is a man not only different from other men but superior, because he possesses a treasure which can never really be shared with them; the scientist leads a life which is of a finer essence than theirs, a life in which reason and action are at one. By the special nature of his experience, the scientist is akin to the artist: ". . . In their extraordinarily different ways, in their lives that have increasingly divergent character, there is still a sensed bond, a sensed analogy. Both the man of science and the man of art live always at the edge of mystery, surrounded by it; both always, as the measures of their creation, have had to do with the harmonization of what is new with what is familiar, with the balance between novelty and synthesis, with the struggle to make partial order in total chaos. They can make the paths which connect the villages of arts and sciences with each other and with the world at large the multiple, varied, precious bonds of a true and worldwide community."

Invested with a special and almost mystical vocation in life, the scientist, without assuming direct responsibility for matters of state, will nonetheless act as counselor, exemplar, source of inspiration: he will play the same part as Oppenheimer did after resigning as director at Los Alamos, until he was thrown down from his pedestal by the Personnel Committee of the Atomic Energy Commission.

Others besides Oppenheimer—scientists, thinkers, imaginative writers—have dreamed of a *sophocratic* society, and have written about it at length. It is an ideal which springs naturally to birth from the contrast between scientific conduct—with its rational procedures, emotional serenity and efficient expenditure of effort—and the unreason, disorder, passion and violence which characterize the history of human societies. It is also a reaction against the stupidity of political rulers, their failure to understand the needs and aims of scientists, their wretched parsimony toward research; and against the police state, with its tyranny and persecution. An eminent British astronomer, Fred Hoyle, who writes science fiction novels in his spare time, has developed this pleasing pipe dream at some length in a curious tale entitled *The Black Cloud*; the book contains an appeal, "Scientists of the world, unite!", which is intended as something more than just an amusing parody. Seizing the opportunity offered when a cataclysm threatens the earth, a scientist assumes power and dictates policy to the governments of the time for the good of humanity as a whole. His death, which borders on the supernatural, results from his having climbed too high and sought to acquire supraterrestrial knowledge.

The disaster which overtook Oppenheimer was less grandiose: it was spawned by the card indexes and reports of F.B.I. agents and McCarthyite witch-hunters. It struck down not only the man but the myth of the essential harmony between the philosophical scientist and the political power of American democracy.

In the name of this power, Oppenheimer had constructed the first atomic bombs. He had been a party to the decision to drop them on the Japanese civilian population. He had stood aside from the efforts made by the majority of United States scientists to convince public opinion that governments must be compelled to abandon these weapons of wholesale destruction. And he had eventually pronounced in favor of making the thermonuclear bomb.

When official ostracism came upon him in 1953 he reacted with a certain dignity, supported by the active solidarity of the very men from whose anti-nuclear struggle he had dissociated himself. No doubt he found time in which to meditate on the judgment which, for his B.B.C. listeners, he had passed on "the increasingly expert destruction of man's spirit by the powers of police, more wicked if not more awful than the ravages of nature's own hand . . .". At the moment when he was speaking those words in London, the dossiers prepared by Colonel Pash were lying on President Eisenhower's desk.

Since then his attitude toward the holders of power has been aloof, to the point of declaring that in relation to the problems now confronting humanity all governments are "cruelly anachronistic". But he still professes the commonplaces of the conventional anti-Communist line.

Oppenheimer and Soviet Science. This conformism has strongly affected his judgment of the scientific situation in the U.S.S.R. In 1945, he was still sufficiently well informed of the state of Soviet research not to share the optimism of American officials, who considered that the Russians would be incapable of tapping nuclear energy for many years to come. General Groves told a Congress committee at the time: "At best, the Soviets will need fifteen or twenty years. . . ." At the beginning of 1953, after the first Soviet thermonuclear tests, Oppenheimer estimated that the U.S.S.R. was four years behind the United States, and based his assessment on the future on the assumption that this lag would persist. He was not trying to reassure his compatriots; on the contrary, he explained that if the stock of bombs on both sides exceeded a certain level both countries would be destroyed; the inequality would make no difference. However, this belief that the Russian atomic scientists had fallen behind was not based on reality. Oppenheimer's appreciation was swayed by the system of values which he had accepted for judging Soviet society.

Soviet nuclear physics had begun developing about 1930, chiefly at the Physico-technical Institute of Kharkov, under the direction of Igor Kurtchatov. The first cyclotron to be put into action in Europe—earlier than that of Joliot at the Collège de France—was at the Radium Institute in Leningrad. Another giant cyclotron was built just before the war, at the Leningrad Physico-technical Institute. In 1939 Brodsky published a paper on the separation of uranium isotopes; and Kurtchatov and Frenkel, at about the same time as Bohr and Frisch, gave a theoretical explanation of the fission of the uranium nucleus. In 1940 Kurtchatov published a study on chain reaction and the Soviet Academy of Sciences announced the setting up of a special uranium commission. The Christmas number of *Izvestia* published an article entitled "Uranium 235," which stated: "Mankind will discover a new source of energy which will surpass all previous sources millions of times over. . . . Man's powers are entering a new age . . . man will be able to produce unlimited energy and employ it in whatever way he chooses."

If it is remembered that at that time Einstein and the European atomic scientists who had fled to America were struggling to make the Washington authorities admit the importance of nuclear research, it becomes clear that the Soviet "lag" was merely a figment of the prevailing political mythology. It is usually idle to reshape the course of history by speculating on what would have resulted if such and such an event had not taken place; but we may regard it as very probable that only Hitler's invasions prevented the first nuclear reactors from being built in Europe—by Joliot in France, and Kurtchatov and his fellow-workers in Russia—instead of by Fermi, in Chicago, in 1942.

The massive but temporary lead held by the United States in 1945 was the combined result of the ruined state of Europe and the gigantic war effort of the U.S.A., an effort undertaken at the instance of refugee scientists from Europe and carried out by expert teams of which those same scientists were the most important members.

Kharkov was in enemy hands, Leningrad was under siege. The Atomic Institute of Moscow began work in the summer of 1943, during the last German offensive in the direction of the capital. In their efforts to achieve chain reaction in uranium fission, the Soviet physicists had to rely on themselves alone. The American authorities were jealously vigilant lest any scientific information find its way to their allies; in Oppenheimer's words, it would have been "high treason." Stalin's spy-mania had deprived the U.S.S.R. of the valuable help of such men as Houtermans. And a country bled white by invasion could not give its scientists material means comparable with those at Oak Ridge and Los Alamos.

Moreover, it seems that during the war the Soviets turned their attention to fundamental research into the structure of the nucleus, on the one hand, and to the possibilities of using nuclear fission as a source of industrial energy, on the other. It was after the destruction of Hiroshima and Nagasaki—whose real significance obviously did not escape the Soviet rulers—that Kurtchatov was ordered to make an atom bomb in the shortest possible space of time. Two years later, in 1947, Molotov announced that the "secret" of the atom bomb was a secret no longer. And in 1949 Oppenheimer was a member of the commission which studied the photographic plates brought back from the upper atmosphere by American bombers, plates which recorded signs of the first Soviet atomic explosion. The former chief of the Los Alamos super-laboratory was in a better position than anybody else to understand that the four years which had elapsed since the Alamogordo test in no way represented a permanent difference between the levels of scientific advance in the two countries. On the contrary, it meant that the Russians had overcome the handicap incurred during the years of war and invasion, overcome it so quickly that there was reason to wonder whether they might not draw ahead in the race. And this did in fact happen when, in 1953, the Russians exploded the first real thermonuclear bomb—the American device which was exploded at Eniwetok was not a transportable projectile. It happened again in August, 1954, when, near Moscow, Ivan Kurtchatov set up the first nuclear power station, with a yield of 5,000 kilowatts.

The mental attitude dominant in America at that time was such that the superiority attained by the Soviet physicists was unthinkable. An explanation was needed; and so the Rosenbergs, charged with having "betrayed the secret of the bomb," were offered up as a sacrifice to the myth of American invincibility.

Though he did not share General Groves' illusions, Oppenheimer was by no means proof against the surrounding pressure of ideas; that was why he too made the mistake of underestimating Soviet science. His own system of political philosophy gives him a bias in this direction. If the development of science is bound up with that of a "liberal" society based on traditional American standards, and if the Soviet system is a fabric of terror, compulsion and ridiculous dogmatism, it can be assumed *a priori* that science in the U.S.S.R. is bound to lag behind that of other countries, particularly the United States. This conviction is so firmly anchored in Oppenheimer's mind that even the force of facts cannot make him revise it. In April 1958—six months after the launching of the first sputnik—when he was asked whether recent Soviet scientific achievements did not invalidate his previous utterances on the subject, he answered awkwardly: "They do seem to invalidate them in part. I am nevertheless convinced that in the domain of pure science the results gained by those of whose immense abilities I am aware, will not stand comparison with what might have been achieved through contact with the West. The handicap of isolation has been great for those scientists. As for the physicists, it seems certain that they have won a certain liberty, private liberty and liberty to work. This is not the case with many of their colleagues, in biology and medicine for example."

Is the scientist responsible? We seem to have strayed a long way from the problem with which this chapter began, that of the moral responsibility of the scientist who created the weapons of mass extermination. But this problem is inseparable from another: the nature of political power. It was because he regarded the possibility of a nuclear victory by the Nazis as a prospect of absolute evil that Einstein urged Roosevelt not to let Hitler obtain a monopoly of the bomb.

Oppenheimer's attitude to the war period, like his attitude to power, seems to have become more detached with the passage of time. Questioned about the Interim Committee, whose crowning action was to advise President Truman to use the bomb, he gave an answer which might be interpreted either as expressing regret or as an attempt at self-justification: time, he said, had unfortunately been lacking; it now seemed that a longer and deeper study of the problem might have led those responsible at the time to form a more precise, or even an entirely different, view of what ought to be done with these new weapons. And when the Franck report was quoted, he rather surprisingly declared that, for his own part, he would not feel able, even after so many years, to assume the responsibility which had fallen to the United States in 1945. Yet there is no doubt that Oppenheimer did assume that responsibility, by his share in ensuring the rejection of the Franck report; its acceptance might have averted the destruction of Hiroshima and perhaps even the arms race which followed.

He assumed it by virtue of the fact that the members of the Interim Committee were serving not as scientists but as technical advisers to the government, and that the advice for which they were asked, in whatever terms the questions might be framed, inescapably implied an act of political choice. It was the same for the authors of the Franck report, who made the opposite choice. In the context, both were acting not as scientists, disinterested seekers after truth, but as citizens whose specialized professional knowledge qualified them to advise in a matter of supreme national importance.

Oppenheimer frequently draws attention to the essential distinction between the scientist's responsibilities and those of the statesman and politician. The scientist's knowledge gives him no special right to control public affairs. Neither can he be called to account for the beneficial or harmful uses to which society may put his findings, but only for the scientific value of those findings.

This view is certainly closer to real life than were the noble dreams of Heisenberg and Bohr, who hoped for a kind of international order of scientists to prevent the misuse of nuclear energy and ensure world peace.

It is also healthier than what he has had to say on various occasions about the scientist's way of life as an example to others. While not denying the lofty plane on which many scientists have lived, one cannot but feel that the impression he conveys is slightly idealized by comparison with what actually goes on in scientific circles, especially university circles. The ordinary human weaknesses are not unknown there—jealousy, rivalry, feelings of frustration, and the influence of self-interest or irrational likes and dislikes on interpersonal relationships.

If we examine the individual attitudes of atomic physicists during the dramatic years so brilliantly described by Robert Jungk, we see these men being tossed this way and that, divided and agitated; swayed, like everybody else, by the political forces in play. The tape recordings of Oppenheimer's interrogations by the military police show that scientific competence does not necessarily endow a man with steadfastness and an unfailing moral stature. It would be chimerical to hope that scientists, as a group within society, will ever exert a decisive influence on public issues; equally, it is unfair to credit them with superhuman responsibilities, like those attributed by primitive tribes to their medicine men and magicians. Scientists' professional activities, like anyone else's, form part of a social structure and are subject to political authority. Scientists, like anyone else, may behave in one way or another in relation to that structure and that authority. And it is true that their choice of behavior, like their work itself, will often have important consequences. But science is not the only important social activity. It is worth pointing these things out; they help one to deflate certain rather over-dramatic presentations of the mission of the scientist in the modern world, such as one reads in the pages of Oppenheimer himself and in those of Jungk and other commentators.

At the same time it remains true that the increasingly large role played by science and technology in human life often intensifies the importance of the decisions which a scientist, as a human being, is called upon to take. This is singularly well illustrated by the history of Robert Oppenheimer. Viewed in itself, it is the story of one of the most eminent contemporary teachers of physics, whom circumstances led to take command, on behalf of his government, of the greatest laboratory ever seen, in order to devise an instrument of mass destruction and world leadership. Perhaps, as some people have accused him of doing, he did then see himself as God, until he was eventually set upon by the authorities whom he had served. Viewed as an example of the moral responsibility of the scientist, the "Oppenheimer case" presents a number of points for study. In 1942 there were very few scientists who would not have contributed with all their might to an endeavor designed to destroy the power of Nazism. But there were also very few who, like Oppenheimer, took it on themselves to assist the witch-hunt. And though they were seriously under-informed about the state of the military situation in the Far East, the majority of atomic physicists, after the Alamogordo test, viewed with great repugnance the possible use of the bomb against civilians. Their opposition would have been practically unanimous if they had known the truth, of which the members of the Interim Committee cannot have been entirely ignorant. The man who pressed the button was President Truman. It may be assumed that the authorities, when selecting scientists to advise them, had picked out those whose views were most likely to conform to the general trend of government policy, and that the real decisions were never in fact in scientific hands. One wonders what would have happened if Oppenheimer had firmly opposed the atomic bombardment of Japanese cities; would it have taken place, or not?

The question makes it hard for us to go on acquitting the scientist of responsibility for the results of his actions. The plane to which those results belong is no longer only that of research and discovery; it is political and moral. Oppenheimer's attitude—namely that he had served merely as a technical adviser, and that the government must bear the whole responsibility for deciding to use the bomb—is a good deal less than convincing. When the scientist uses his knowledge to support the activities of authority or to influence them in one direction or another, he places himself in a position which automatically invalidates the fundamental distinction (which we discussed and accepted in an earlier section) between the researcher and the ordinary citizen. This predicament, in an age of nuclear energy and inter-continental ballistic missiles, is no longer unusual. The physicist taking the atomic nucleus to pieces is not a superman —neither an example to guide the rest of us, nor a special being with the right to shut himself up in his laboratory as in an ivory tower. What, then, ought he to do? What is his role in society?

Frédéric Joliot used to propound an attractive thesis: that science is misused by those forces which are hostile to peace and progress. According to this view, any practical application of knowledge is legitimate and normal if it serves the arts of peace and makes mankind happier; any application which serves destructive ends is abnormal and perverse. Joliot consequently declared that he would never take part in constructing an atomic bomb. At the time and in the setting in which he was speaking, the great Communist scientist could make such a resolve without inconsistency. But it is obvious that, in different circumstances, he could not have maintained it without adopting the extreme pacifist position of absolute nonviolence (which was not his attitude to life). For, though all violence is destructive and inherently hateful, we sometimes find ourselves having to use it—or thinking that we have to use it—in order to ward off some yet more hateful violence. That was the intention of the Los Alamos atomic scientists. The crucial question is whether they were right, or until what point in the course of events they were right, and to answer it is to make an act of political choice. The abuse of science began on the day when a primitive tribe first burned down the huts of an enemy tribe, instead of confining the use of fire to clearing the bush. And the abuse of science will cease when humanity rises to a level of social organization on which there is no longer any room for violence and destruction.

Must we say, then, that the progress of science has nothing to contribute to our efforts to make a better world? Oppenheimer, pessimist though he is, has perhaps expressed, almost in spite of himself, such reasons as we can find for hopefulness. His analysis of the intellectual and moral values inherent in scientific research is both clear and valid: science means rejecting dogmatism, it means respecting truth and seeking it patiently; science is reason and effectiveness. It is by applying these values to the whole life of the mind, and to the shaping of his own destiny, that man will attain to a higher pattern of life. Our scientists—dependent as they now are on governments, military bodies and social forces which at one moment persecute them and, at another, control them by dispensing the facilities for their work—have to ask themselves who is going to protect and promote the values which they appreciate more vividly and prize more intensely than anyone else. The problem of the future relationship of scientists to governmental power really comes down to the question: what kind of power? and with what future in view?

SELECTED WRITINGS

The Tree of Knowledge

> In April 1958 Dr. Oppenheimer spoke to a group
> of editors and journalists from all over the world
> who had gathered in Washington for a meeting
> of the International Press Institute. He spoke with-
> out a prepared text, using only notes; the article
> below is published substantially as it was recorded
> during the lecture.

WHEN I speak to the press I am aware that I am talking to a
group of men who have a singularly critical destiny in these
rather peculiar times. Those of us whose work it is to preserve old learning, and to find new, look to the press to keep
the channels of truth and communication open and to keep
men in some sense united in common knowledge and common humanity.

I want to talk about the nature and structure of our
knowledge today and how it has altered and complicated
the problems of the press. There are enormous differences
between our world of learning today—our Tree of Knowledge—and those of Athens, or the Enlightenment, or the
dawn of science in fifteenth- and sixteenth-century Europe.
You can get some suggestion of how shattering these changes
have been if you remember that Plato, when he tried to
think about human salvation and government, recommended
mathematics as one of the ways to learn to know the truth,
to discriminate good from evil and the wise from the fool-

ish. Plato was not a creative mathematician, but students confirm that he knew the mathematics of his day, and understood it, and derived much from it.

Today, it is not only that our kings do not know mathematics, but our philosophers do not know mathematics and —to go a step further—our mathematicians do not know mathematics. Each of them knows a branch of the subject and they listen to each other with a fraternal and honest respect; and here you find a knitting together of the different fields of mathematical specialization. In fact, a great deal of progress in mathematics is a kind of over-arching generalization which brings things that had been separate into some kind of relation. Nevertheless, it is not likely today that our most learned advisers—the men who write in the press and tell us what we may think—would suggest that the next President of the United States be able to understand the mathematics of the day.

YIELDING BOUNDARIES

The first characteristic of scientific knowledge today—a trivial and pedestrian characteristic—is that its growth can be measured. When I talk of "science" here I would like to use the word in the broadest sense to include all man's knowledge of his history and behavior, his knowledge, in fact, of anything that can be talked of in an objective way so that people all over the world can understand it, know what the scientist has done, reproduce it, and find out if it is true or not. It is hard to measure the growth of science defined in these terms in a sensible way but it can be measured in fairly foolish ways.

One way of measuring science, for example, is to find out how many people are engaged in it. I know a young historian of science who has amused himself by counting the scientists of the last two centuries and he has found that their number has, quite accurately, doubled about every ten years. Professor Purcell of Harvard put the same conclusion another way the other day when he said, "Ninety per cent of all scientists are alive." This gives some notion of the changes involved.

I must, however, qualify this trend in two ways. First, it cannot continue, because if it went on for another century, then everyone would be a scientist—there would be nobody else left. So a kind of saturation is setting in and the rate of science's growth is slowing down. The second qualification is that what might be called the "stature" of science is not proportional to its volume; it may be proportional to the cube root of its volume or something like that. In short, every scientist is not a Newton and the proportion of Newtons among all scientists tends to decline as the number of people involved gets bigger.

Despite all qualification, though, the fact remains that the growth in the number of people in science and the growth in firm knowledge—important, non-trivial knowledge of the kind that appears in learned journals and books—have been more or less parallel; and this growth will continue, although the increase in it is bound to taper off. The result is that nearly everything that is now known was not in any book when most of us went to school; we cannot know it unless we have picked it up since. This in itself presents a problem of communication that is nightmarishly formidable.

On the other hand, there is a more encouraging aspect of this scientific knowledge. As it grows, things, in some ways, get much simpler. They do not get simpler because one discovers a few fundamental principles which the man in the street can understand and from which he can derive everything else. But we do find an enormous amount of order. The world is not random and whatever order it has seems in large part "fit", as Thomas Jefferson said, for the human intelligence. The enormous variety of facts yield to some kind of arrangement, simplicity, generalization.

One great change in this direction—and it has not yet, I think, fully come to public understanding—is that we are beginning to see that the hard boundaries which once seemed to separate the parts of the natural world from each other are now yielding to some kind of inquiry. We are beginning to see ways across the gaps between the living and the dead, the physical and the mental.

Let me give just a few illustrations:

It is probably not an accident, although it is not really understood, that the age of the earth—some six or seven billion years according to calculation by radioactivity techniques—is very close to the period required for the most distant nebulae to recede into the furthest reaches of space. We can picturesquely define that time by saying that during it things were a lot closer together than they are now and the state of the material universe was very different. Some years ago the brilliant Russian biochemist Oparin suggested that when the atmosphere had no oxygen in it, certain conditions could have prevailed on earth under which life could have originated from inorganic matter. There has since been confirmation in Urey's laboratory and this hypothesis turns out to be true. Although mermaids and heroes do not walk out of the test tube, we do see that quite reasonable accounts of the origin of life are not too far from our grasp.

The recent research on how the genetic mechanism of all living material operates shows how certain proteins have special information-bearing properties—how they can store information and transmit it from one generation to another.

The study of how the nerve impulses from our sense organs to the brain can be modulated and altered by the perceptive apparatus of the animal—often it is an animal rather than a man—gives us some notion both of the unreliability of our sense impressions and of the subtlety of the relations between thought and the object of thought.

All these problems, which even in the nineteenth century seemed to obstruct the possibility of a unified view of the great arch of nature, are yielding to discovery; and in all science there is a pervasive, haunting sense that no part of nature is really irrelevant to any other.

GAY AND WONDERFUL MYSTERY

But the model of science which results from all this investigation is entirely different from a model which would have seemed natural and understandable to the Greeks or the Newtonians. Although we do not start from common human experience, as they did, we so refine what we think, we so change the meaning of words, we build up so distinctive a tradition, that scientific knowledge today is not an enrichment of the general culture. It is, on the contrary, the possession of countless, highly specialized communities who love it, would like to share it, would very much like to explain it, and who make some efforts to communicate it; but it is not part of the common human understanding. This is the very strange predicament to which the press addresses itself today and to which it can give, I believe, only a partial solution.

It would of course be splendid—and one often hears this —if we could say that while we cannot know the little details about the workings of atoms and proteins and the human psyche, we *can* know the fundamental principles of science. But I am afraid that this is only marginally true. The fundamentals of physics are defined in terms of words that refer to an experience that lay people have not had and that very few people have run across in their education.

For example, in my opinion, it is almost impossible to explain what the fundamental principle of relativity is about, and this is even more true of the quantum theory. It is only possible to use analogies, to evoke some sense of understanding. And as for the recent discovery—the very gay and wonderful discovery for which Dr. Yang and Dr. Lee were awarded the Nobel Prize—that nature has a preference for right-handed or left-handed screws in certain situations and is not indifferent to the handedness of the screw—to explain this is, I believe, quite beyond my capacity. And I have never heard anyone do it in a way that could be called an enrichment of culture.

To sum up the characteristics of scientific knowledge today, then, I would say that it is mostly new; it has not been digested; it is not part of man's common knowledge; it has become the property of specialized communities who may on occasions help one another but who, by and large, pursue their own way with growing intensity further and further from their roots in ordinary life.

We must always remember that, like most human accomplishments, the sciences have grown out of a long, accumulating experience of error, astonishment, invention, and understanding. Taken as a whole, they constitute a series of traditions; and these traditions—once largely common, now largely separate—are as essential to understanding a part of biology or astronomy or physics as the general human tradition is to the existence of civilized life. I know that a complete immersion in these many different, related, yet specific traditions is beyond the reach of any one person—that as things stand today, most of us are without any experience, really, in any. We have much in common from the simple ways in which we have learned to live and talk and work together. Out of this have grown the specialized disciplines like the fingers of the hand, united in origin but no longer in contact.

PRACTICAL BOOBY TRAPS

Now I am going to make a distinction which may seem arbitrarily sharp but which is I think important both to the learned community and the press. I have been talking until now about science as the things we have discovered about nature—incredible things and beautiful and astonishing, but defined, usually, not by any use to which they are put, but simply in terms of the ways in which they were found out. Pure science is thus inherently circumscribed but immensely revealing, showing as it does that left to itself, man's imagination was not a patch on reality.

Seeking out this knowledge is one problem and I am not through with it. But the other problem is that, of course, this knowledge has practical consequences. On it is built the world we live in and the face of that world has been changed, probably more than in any other period of history, by the scientific revolution. Now these practical consequences, because they are intended in some way to be responsive to man's needs, can be talked about in an intelligible way. It is not necessary to know how a nucleus is put together, or what are the laws which determine its behavior, in order to explain what nuclear energy is all about. It may be very hard to explain it well because it involves human choices, options, decisions, prejudices. But I believe that it is no more difficult to write about nuclear energy than about where people go for a holiday. It is not much harder to write about nuclear weapons, except that, to the problems of human variety, there is added the problem of a very great deal of secrecy.

To take another example, it has not been hard to write about the use of vaccines in the prevention of disease and these can be described without elaborate theory. As a matter of fact the vaccines were discovered without much theoretical background and the atomic bomb was made before we had much idea what held nuclei together; we do not have very much idea today.

The press has done an admirable job in explaining these and other practical applications of science—I think it is aware that it has to do a much, much greater one. But there are, I think, some booby traps which stand in its way. I would like to list three of them.

One of the simplest traps is that when technical people talk they always emphasize the fact that they are not sure. Sometimes, as in the case of knowing all the effects of radiation on life, we are not, in fact, sure, because experience takes so long to acquire. But usually the statement that we are not sure is more like the polite comment, "I don't want to bore you but . . ." Statements about scientific matters are not entirely sure—nothing is—but compared to politics they are so extremely sure as to be of a different order of certainty. If a scientist says he is not sure, pay attention to the limits within which he says this—the margin for error he insists on allowing. This margin will not be so wide. Within what limits we are uncertain about the genetic damages of radiation, for example, is not something to worry or wonder about. We know something of the effects on the genes. The differences of opinion over this question lie in quite a different field. They lie in conflicting assessments of the relative gravity of these damages and of other vaster dangers of total nuclear war.

A second trap to beware of is the strange fact that the words scientists use have taken on a special meaning so that there is a confusing quality of punning when they discuss technical things and describe their aims. "Relativity" sounds like something that occurs in daily life; it is not. Scientists talk about the "adventure" of science and they are right; but of course in the public mind this is very likely to be identified with looking to see if the other side of the moon is really there. Here the public is wrong. The adventures of science are intellectual adventures, involving discoveries of the inadequacy of our means of describing nature, because it is so unfamiliar and strange. Space travel has, no doubt, its value and virtue, but it is in no way related to the great adventures of science. It would be, of course, if we could go out two or three billion light-years and see what is going on there, because it is hard to see that far with telescopes. But this is not the same thing as the progress of human learning and understanding.

A third trap and a serious one—it has infested the discussion of radioactive fallout—is that in most technical explanations, very large numbers occur, and it is often hard to convey their implications sensitively. It may be equally true to say, for instance, that something will cause 10,000 casualties and that these casualties will affect a hundred-thousandth of the population of the world; but one statement can make the effect seem rather small and the other can make it very big. We cannot get over the habit of talking in numbers but it takes some exposition if we are to avoid creating the wrong impression.

I have one example of this. It has to do with radioactive fallout. I know nothing about the main efforts being made to eliminate fallout at present but it is obvious that they have to do with the elimination of fissionable material from bombs. The first step is to take the casing away from big bombs and the next step, presumably, is to take away much— or even all—of the rest.

I have some understanding of this as a technical problem and some idea of the benefits which will accrue from it. But in an old day, when we had the first primitive, tiny, atomic weapons, there was also a contrast. The story is in the public domain and I am surprised that no reporter has dug it out. We were thinking then in terms of casualties of hundreds of thousands and not hundreds of millions. It was a much more innocent age but it was warfare and in that sense it was not innocent. All the bombs then had fissionable material and the first one we set off at Trinity near Los Alamos was dirty. It was set off practically at ground level, the fireball touched the ground and in fact a great deal of radioactive contamination was spread, by the standard of those days. The government had a lot of trouble with a herd of cattle whose hair turned white as a result. It was a very dirty bomb.

The bombs at Hiroshima and Nagasaki on the other hand were clean. They were exploded high in the air and few if any casualties were produced by fallout. Possibly there were a handful on a global scale, but practically all the hundreds of thousands who died, and the others who were maimed from radiation and blast, did not have the benefit of fallout. Nevertheless, I vastly prefer our first dirty bomb to those two clean ones.

When all is said and done about these problems—essentially soluble problems—of describing the practical consequences of scientific progress, there remains the central perplexing question, to which I keep returning, of bringing an appreciation of the new scientific knowledge to the world. It is a question of high importance; it deserves study.

I do not see, for example, how the scientist can evoke the same understanding and grateful warmth from his fellows as the actor who gives them pleasure and insight, and reveals their own predicament to them, or the musician or dancer or writer or athlete, in whom they see their talents in greater perfection, and often their own limitations and error in larger perspective. The power of the new knowledge itself to excite the intelligent public's mind is very different from the days of Newton when the problems under discussion—the course of the heavenly bodies, the laws of dynamics—were not far from ordinary human experience. People could go to demonstrations to see the new principles in action; they could discuss them in salons and cafés. The ideas were revolutionary but not very hard to understand. It is no wonder that the excitement and change and enrichment of culture in Europe that came about as a result of these discoveries were without parallel.

Today there are sciences like that, which are just starting. During the nineteenth century the theory of evolution certainly played this role. And today, in the psychological sciences there are many fundamental points that anyone can understand if he is willing to take the trouble—science here is just beginning to leave the common experience, and the accumulated tradition has not yet grown very far.

Yet as a whole, the problem is formidable. It is not hopeless—much can and should be done. But I do not believe it can be done by the press alone. Part of the solution lies in education, and, I think, part of it lies with just learning to live with it. Our tradition and culture and community of learning have become reticulated, complicated, and non-hierarchical. They have their own nobility if one brings to them the right attitudes of affection, interest, and indefatigability. The new knowledge is not the kind of thing one can ever finally master; there is no place a man can go to get it all straight. But it has its beauty if one knows how to live with it. And the main thing is to recognize this and not to talk in terms of cultures which are unattainable for us, but to welcome those that are at hand.

Because beyond the need for explanation of the practical, beyond the need for information, there will always be the need for a community of meaning and understanding. To my mind this is a basic and central need. It is a very grave circumstance of our time that the overwhelming part of new knowledge is available only to a few people and does not enrich common understanding. I think, nevertheless, that learned folk do have some sense of this community; and I think this furnishes a clue for others, because it comes in part from the similarities of experience in our professional lives—from recognizing points in common and differences in our separate traditions. We have lived in parallel ways through experience and wonder and have some glimmering of a kind of new-found harmony.

This suggests to me that all of us in our years of learning, and many if not most of us throughout our lives, need some true apprenticeship, some hard and concentrated work, in the specialized traditions. This will make us better able to understand one another but, most important of all, it will clarify for us the extent to which we do not understand one another. It will not be easy. It means a major change in the way we look at the world and in our educational practices. It means that an understanding of the scope, depth, and nature of our ignorance should be among the primary purposes of education. But to me, it seems necessary for the coherence of our culture, and for the very future of any free civilization. A faithful image of this in the public press could do a great deal to help us all get on with it.

CRAZY BUT NOT STUPID

I want to turn now to a second subject—disarmament—which may seem irrelevant but, as I hope to show, is not entirely so. Somehow it does not seem quite right of me to discuss a question which I regard as quite central for the future of culture without adding at least a few phrases about the anomalous and terrible situation of the new weapons with which, in their origins, I had quite a close connection.

Perhaps I can best start with a story. It seems that a man was driving into an American city to keep an appointment and one of his back wheels came off in front of an insane asylum. One of the inmates stared out of the window at him and the man said to him in desperation, "Look, the bolts are missing from one of my wheels—I've got an important engagement and everything depends on my making it." The man in the asylum said, "Well you've got four wheels, take a bolt from each of the other three and your problem is solved." The traveler looked up and said, "Say, you aren't so crazy." And the inmate replied, "Sure I'm crazy, but I'm not stupid." That may be a good parable for where we stand with our weapons.

I fully respect those who take the cheerful view that matters might be much worse. It would certainly be worse if all Europe were in Communist hands; it would be worse if a third world war had broken out and ravaged our lives and our culture. But the situation is still terribly dangerous. When we come on testimony before Congressional committees that our operations as now planned would call for 300 million deaths, and so on, we are not, I believe, hearing overstatements or misstatements.

Furthermore, it is my impression that those who are in a position to know expect that, for a time at least, technical developments may tend to create a situation much more trigger-happy and much less subject to the enormous control those weapons call for—the control which should perhaps be the first expression of that change in the behavior of states and governments for which we are surely destined if we are to survive.

Yet there is enough anxiety so that there is more and more talk of disarmament, and the governments—which have agonizing responsibilities for maintaining the power and influence of their states—are at last nibbling gently at the subject.

I would be reluctant to create the impression that I do not believe in disarmament. We all know what indescribable difficulties stand in the way of negotiating it and how Utopian it seems to talk of meaningful, effective, adequate disarmament which would protect the world. But my point is a little different. It is not that disarmament is Utopian but that it really is not Utopian enough. There are two quite simple arguments from the nature of scientific progress which bear on the stability and value of disarmament. They are very general principles and they were very much on our minds when, in 1946, a group of people in this country and abroad tried to work out an idea of what the control of atomic energy would mean.

The first point, which I mentioned earlier, is that new discoveries are made with such enormous and unpredictable rapidity that you cannot possibly devise an instrument of disarmament which is to hold good twenty or thirty years from now unless you forbid inquiry and discovery—and you probably could not legislate that even if you wanted to.

The second point is that the acquisition of knowledge is, for practical purposes, and barring global catastrophe, an irreversible thing. If ever the nations do start to fly at each other's throats they will be quite capable of doing again whatever they once learned to do.

AN OPEN WORLD

These two propositions meant to us then, and mean to me now, that the world has to be an open world in which, practically speaking, secrets are illegal. They mean that some of the great power and responsibility which habitually and traditionally rest with the nation-states must rest in less national hands which are better able to use it. They mean that ours must be a united world, as it has never been before.

Some part of this redistribution of power can be accomplished through international organizations, and the experience of OEEC and EURATOM and NATO give very great hope for developing into valuable trans-national institutions. NATO, in particular, may have its greatest historic destiny in this hope, rather than in its past.

But, even more than a growing role for the international organizations, these propositions signify to me the greater development of something which pervades the whole of natural science, and most of learning, and which is beginning even to touch our colleagues behind the Iron Curtain. I refer to the fraternal communities of men embarked on specialized work: those who know how to extirpate malaria; those who seek to understand the radio signals coming to us from remote parts of the Universe; those who recreate the early history of man, his art, and his learning. Their knowledge and know-how bind them together as possessors of true community, complementary to the local geographic communities, complementary to the communities of state and civic tradition; they are the warp of community, as the nations are the woof.

These communities of the mind are the human counterpart and the basis of the international institutions that the future must hold in store and on them rests, it seems to me, the hope that we will survive this unprecedented period in the history of man.

(From *Harper's Magazine*, October 1958)

Spiritual Disquiet

A CONVERSATION

"Do you consider that moral confusion and spiritual disquiet are new feelings for scientists to have? and to what, in the present-day development of science, do you attribute them?"

"Yes, this feeling is a new one, and atomic scientists are not the only ones to experience it. It springs essentially from the prodigious growth of science in recent years.

"This scientific upsurge has been accompanied by a degree of specialization so intense that no one man today can master more than a minute fraction of the existing sum of knowledge. This gives rise to a feeling of ignorance and solitude whose intensity seems to be proportional to the individual's knowledge. Scientists today are filled with longing for that single key, that central axis common to all branches of knowledge, in which their ancestors believed but which we shall never be able to recover.

"In the case of atomic scientists, this distress has been augmented by fear of a weapon of whose horrific nature no numerical statement has given an exaggerated impression, and by the confusion which any honorable man must feel when he finds himself called upon to wield power. Men trained for a career in pure science were in no way prepared for the responsibilities they were obliged to assume."

"Is it your opinion that present-day knowledge in theoret-

141

ical physics proves what the various religions have long de-clared, namely that human faculties of observation and judg-ment possess insuperable limits?"

"The idea of scientific progress seems to me to have be-come indissolubly linked with the notion of human destiny. To me, this conception appears to be alien to religion. The development of science has underlined the discrepancy be-tween the theoretically unlimited possibilities of knowledge and the limited capacities of mankind, between the infinite accessibility of the universe and our own immediate nature. The possibilities for knowledge remain unlimited, even if in future they are confined to a minority of more and more highly specialized researchers. Thus some of the abysses which, in the 19th century, seemed destined forever to cut us off from a unified vision of nature, have lately been crossed; recent work on the age of the earth, on the transi-tion from inorganic to organic existence, on the properties of certain proteins which genetically transmit or preserve an acquired experience from one generation to another, and on the nature of nervous impulses, are so many bridges into the unknown."

"Some people aspire toward the creation of a new spiritual outlook which would render possible a contemporary syn-thesis, a unification of all knowledge. Do you consider such a synthesis belongs, rather, to the realm of science?"

"This idea of a synthesis appears to me to be based on a typological error concerning the structure of knowledge it-self. Our knowledge will never again, in my belief, bear an all-embracing character. It will continue to be divided be-tween potential and actual; supposedly all-embracing knowl-edge will be meaningless or will turn into dogmatism, for lack of proper means of evaluation. Our knowledge today can no longer constitute, as knowledge did in Athens or 15th-century Europe, an enrichment of general culture. It will con-tinue to be the privilege of small, highly specialized groups, which will no longer be able to render it accessible to hu-manity at large as Newton's knowledge was rendered acces-sible.

"It seems to me completely impossible, for example, to explain the fundamental principle of relativity, the quantum theory or the principle of complementarity, and I have never heard an exposition of these subjects which could be considered an enrichment of culture.

"As for the revival of a spiritual attitude, I fear we shall never again see a period comparable to your marvelous 13th century in France. We are condemned to live in a world where every question we ask leads to another, and so *in infinitum*. One of the distressing characteristics of knowledge is its irreversibility.

"I am afraid that all those today who are looking for synthesis or unity are simply trying to put the clock back. I believe they could get their synthesis only at the price of tyranny or renunciation."

"In this world which lacks a synthesis—a world whose nature you yourself are occupied in conveying to others—can scientific experience serve as a guide in finding the new moral attitude which you feel to be necessary?"

"It seems that the only path open to us is the quest for a certain equilibrium, in the achievement and maintenance of which every man of science is continually being exercised. The scientist is forced to find this equilibrium; the discipline of science involves a just discrimination between what is new and what is familiar, between courage and servitude, between the essential and the superfluous. It demands a notion of truth as something completely unambiguous. And ambiguity, in the world of today, can only be a source of confusion. Finally, it necessarily implies a fraternity, a community of thought and action without which man would remain helpless, a prisoner of a too restricted view of the human condition in too vast and complex a universe.

"If the experience of science could be communicated (and it seems to me important that it should be), it would enable us to prepare a larger number of people to confront the difficult situation of 'man before the universe,' a situation in relation to which both philosophers and governments at the present time seem to me to be cruelly anachronistic."

(From a conversation with Dr. Escoffier-Lambotte, reported in *Le Monde,* April 29th, 1958.) [Translated here from the French, since no original in English appears to exist. Tr.]

Science and Our Common Language

Question by Raymond Aron: If, outside of science, all decisions are arbitrary, has the progress of scientific reason merely succeeded in handing over to unreason the most important question of all, namely the definition of the good life and the good society?

Reply by Robert Oppenheimer: The problem I should like to raise in connection with this question is that of the relation between the prodigious strides being made by science in our time, and the weight, the real worth, of the contribution which we may hope this scientific progress has made to our common language.

By "common language" I mean to convey an ideal notion: that part of man's heritage which, without seeking to embrace all possible experience, has the quality of being "public," of expressing in terms intelligible to everyone things which are accessible to everyone and meanings which are comprehensible to everyone.

Today, this image of a "public sector" has been obscured by several factors: the extensiveness of our world and its communities, the egalitarianism which assumes that everybody can take part in discussion, the rapid growth of our societies and the profound changes taking place inside them. But the image has also suffered from another phenomenon: the prodigious development of science and knowledge.

All the great sciences of today are the offspring of philosophical reflection and technical invention. Historians may argue endlessly about the respective importance of these two components, but one thing is certain: the whole of science has its origin in a common, non-specialized language.

If we go back to the dawn of the European tradition or to the beginnings of modern society, we find that knowledge was originally the province of a small number of individuals. The citizen of Athens, the handful of men who concerned themselves with the structure of political power in the United States, the beneficiaries of the 18th century Enlightenment, from Montesquieu to the Revolution—the number was relatively small in each case. They possessed a fairly well assimilated common language, experience and knowledge. No doubt 18th-century physics, astronomy and mathematics were already beginning to take on that character of abstract specialization which is typical of them today, but they were still within the range of any cultivated man.

The situation at the present time is totally different. We observe, indeed, an increasing estrangement between the world of science and that of the common language, the former having impoverished, intimidated and emasculated the second, depriving it of its legitimacy and condemning it to a kind of permanently arbitrary condition. A great chasm has appeared between the intellectual world of the scientist and that of the men who, at the level of the common language, are busy with the fundamental human problems.

One of the reasons is that man's scientific activity has developed, both quantitatively and qualitatively, in a way which would have appeared extremely strange, and even baneful, to Pythagoras and Plato, and a presentiment of which darkened the closing years of the life of Newton.

None of this, you may say, matters very much: there are a few great discoveries, a few great principles, which everyone can understand, and the details are unimportant. Some details are, it is true; but, on the whole, the whole mass of published information within the framework of each science furnishes a fairly accurate picture of what anyone has to learn before proceeding further. And I ask you to believe that the onward march of each of the sciences is bringing us revelations, spectacles of order, harmony and subtlety, occasions of wonder and admiration which are quite comparable to the great discoveries we are taught about at school. But these revelations are not easy to communicate in terms of everyday experience. They belong to particular traditions and are expressed in a language which has been refined, sharpened and corrected over a period of centuries or decades. And that is why, if you were to ask me what are the foundations of science, what science is really about, I should be unable to tell you. If you were to ask me for the great law governing the behavior of atoms, not as we understand that law today but as it was understood at the beginning of the century, I could certainly write it up for you on the blackboard and it would not take up much room. But to make it mean something in your eyes would doubtless be a painful experience both for you and for me.

The ramification of science is something equally hard to understand except for those who live with it. None of us is very closely acquainted with his neighbors in other disciplines. There is, to be sure, a certain amount of interlocking between the branches. As far as I know, there is no danger of contradiction between them. There is a loose kinship running through them all. Analogies—especially formal, mathematical analogies—can be found between such widely distant domains as that of language and that of the internal combustion engine. But there is no logical priority of any one science over any other. The behavior of living matter cannot be deduced from the laws of physics. There is simply an absence of contradiction. The criteria of order, harmony and consistency, which are as important in every discipline as accurate observation and correct reasoning, differ from one science to another. What is considered simple in everyday life is not so in the eyes of the physicist, and vice versa. The concept of simplicity, and the concept of nature, have changed.

To all this must be added the sense of imperfection, of contingency, of endlessness, which arises from the study of nature, a sense which is hard to convey on the common-language level; a sense which is impossible to epitomize, impossible to control, impossible to avoid. It expresses the fact that science is something growing; yet doubtless, at the same time, something whose purposes are ultimately identified with those of civilized life.

This combination of circumstances has contributed to depriving our common language of what was most necessary to it: a basis of common knowledge. I shall not try to evaluate the harmful effects produced on our philosophical thinking by the fact that a whole category of human achievements, born of philosophy and invention, is inaccessible to philosophers and ordinary people. But it is a sad thing—I know it from previous experience—to have to talk about the human situation and to be constrained to say: "I leave aside, I omit, I overlook as unimportant so vast, central, human and moving an element of man's intellectual history as the growth of the sciences."

The problem is no easy one. I do not think it possible to provide every man with sufficient information to form a totally common basis of knowledge. We have not even got such a basis in the sciences. I find it extremely difficult— and on the whole I fail—to understand what modern mathematicians are doing and why they are doing it. I hear with admiring wonder, though as a mere amateur, of what biochemists and biophysicists are bringing to light. But I have one advantage: that of knowing a small part of one subject sufficiently well to have, in the depths of my being, the sense of knowledge and the sense of ignorance. And *that* is perhaps an awareness which it might be altogether impossible to diffuse more widely.

When I speak of a stable, genuinely common tradition, I am of course thinking of an essentially secular philosophy and culture. Not that I wish to overlook or exclude the influence of living revelation, religious inspiration, as part of the sources of our traditions. But I think these influences have been brutally disturbed by the volcanic upheavals of our history.

Everyone knows how ill-prepared we were for the tragedies which the 20th century held in store for us. I am thinking especially of the two world wars and the totalitarian revolutions. Let us take an example. It is incontrovertible that we are living on our inheritance from the Christian tradition. Many of us are believers; none of us is indifferent to the Christian order, to the injunctions and hopes of Christianity. That is why I am profoundly disturbed to note that no moral discussion of any quality or significance has been started on the problem of the new weapons, the atomic weapons.

There have been discussions in terms of security, strategy, force-relationships. But what can we think, what are we to expect of a civilization which has always looked on moral values as an essential element in human life, but which is incapable of envisaging the prospect of an almost universal holocaust except in terms of strategy?

I believe that in 1945, in 1949 and perhaps in the current year, there were decisive moments when the opening of public discussion on the meaning, orientation and values of human life could have profoundly changed the moral climate and future outlook in our time.

I will say just this: every time the West, and more particularly my own country, has expressed the opinion that it is legitimate to employ weapons of mass destruction, provided that they are employed against an adversary who has done something evil, we have been wrong. And I think that our unscrupulousness—which developed during the Second World War, by reason of its total nature and the growing callousness of those in power—has done a grave disservice to the cause of freedom and free men.

The problems I have raised are, I know, discouraging in their complexity: how can we succeed in comprehending a little more of what is going on in the world, and in resting content with a limited comprehension wherever certainty is impossible? But there is one thing I am sure of: that we shall succeed in doing this only in so far as we understand how much effort, discipline and will-power it demands from us. And I find it hard to believe that the common language can attain to a higher level of comprehension unless the doors are opened before it, the doors leading into the domain in which the greatest intellectual activity of our time is being carried on.

(Contribution to the Congress for Cultural Freedom, Rheinfelden; published in *L'Express,* October 15th, 1959.) [Translated here from the French, not reproduced from an English original. Tr.]

A General Glance at Oppenheimer's Thinking

IN addition to a large number of scientific papers (mostly published in the *Physical Review*) and a few articles of a more general kind, Robert Oppenheimer has published two volumes of addresses collected under the titles *Science and the Common Understanding* and *The Open Mind*. It is in this part of his written work, which is comprehensible to any member of the educated public, that he presents the essence of his political and philosophical thinking; he also enlarges, interestingly and at length, on the value of science, especially nuclear physics, in contemporary society.

Science and the Common Understanding consists of his broadcast lectures delivered in London for the B.B.C. in 1953, on the eve of his being summoned before the Personnel Committee of the Atomic Energy Commission. The fact of their having been written for the microphone gives them a clear, loose-jointed style; at the same time they show a high degree of rigor, both in the choice of words and in the logical connection of the themes they handle. The book is a well rounded unity in which, after having outlined the history of physics from Newton to wave mechanics, the author discusses, soberly but at times with considerable feeling, the problems presented today by the relation of the scientist to other people, and of science to society.

The first lecture, *Newton: the Path of Light,* is a kind of philosophical preamble. Oppenheimer inquires "as to whether there are direct connections, and if so of what sort,

151

between the truths that science uncovers and the way men think about things in general—their metaphysics—their ideas about what is real and what is primary. . . ." Such a relationship, if it exists, is far from obvious, as is shown by the errors so frequently made by people who write about the work of the great scientists. Thus, for example, "the belief in physical progress, the bright gaiety, and the relative indifference to religion characteristic of the enlightenment were as foreign to Newton's character and preoccupation as could be; this did not keep the men of the enlightenment from regarding Newton as their patron and prophet."

The vocabulary of science plays tricks on philosophers. Between the atom of the ancient thinkers (and of Newton), and that of contemporary physics, there is a profound difference, almost a contradiction. The first is truly ἄτομος, "that which cannot be cut," the indivisible, elementary particle. To contemporary physics, the atom is a highly complex universe not all of whose constituents have yet been unraveled and whose internal laws have not been fully discovered. Even the elementary particles in which Rutherford and Bohr believed they had discovered the ingredients of the atom, are not truly elementary; the list of particles is still growing, and some kinds of particle turn into others.

There is doubtless no reason for assuming that physicists will never discover the really fundamental particle, the genuine ἄτομος; it can be argued, indeed, that were this ultimate atom to elude all experimental search it might exist none the less. There is nothing in science to prove that it does not—or that it does.

But does not science at least give us some assurance that the external world really exists, whatever else may not do so? Here, Oppenheimer allows himself a momentary metaphysical flight which borders on solipsism. The scientist is naturally aware that his search for truth is based on communication with other people: if "he is a thoughtful man, he may be hesitant to think that only his own consciousness is real and all else illusion. But that view, too, is not by logic exorcised; from time to time it may rule his spirit." A curious remark; one is tempted to relate it to the references which Oppenheimer sometimes makes, unfortunately in rather vague terms, to the philosophies of the East.

If there is no necessary logical connection between scientific knowledge and ordinary people's idea of the world, it is possible nevertheless to find "valid and relevant and greatly needed analogies to human problems lying outside the present domains of science or its present borderlands." Before dealing with these analogies, Oppenheimer reminds us of the development of mechanistic physics after Descartes and Newton. To the thinkers of the eighteenth century, the universe was a vast collection of mechanisms functioning in accordance with rigorous laws, the chief of which was that of universal attraction. If the state it had reached at any one moment were fully known, the whole of its future could be predicted. It was true that such sciences as chemistry and biology did not account for the world in these machinelike terms; however, that was only a temporary shortcoming, the result of inadequate knowledge. "There was the belief that in the end all nature would be reduced to physics, to the giant machine." This is the conception of the objective world which still dominates our thinking. It was naturally associated with the belief in universal reason and, though there is no logical necessity for this connection, with the belief in progress and human perfectibility. Oppenheimer ends his lecture with a quotation from Thomas Jefferson: "I am among those who think well of the human character generally. I consider man as formed for society, and endowed by nature with those dispositions which fit him for society. I believe also, with Condorcet . . . that his mind is perfectible to a degree of which we cannot as yet form any conception. . . . While the art of printing is left to us, science can never be retrograde; what is once acquired of real knowledge can never be lost."

The second lecture, which takes us into the twentieth century, is called *Science as Action*. It poses the problem (which was hardly ever considered in earlier centuries) of the relationship between old and new knowledge. The second does not reject the first, it absorbs and widens it. Moreover, what was an object of discovery yesterday soon becomes an instrument for making further discoveries, a new means of perception and action. The most striking example is the alpha particle which Rutherford discovered and later used for exploring the atomic nucleus. Collisions between alpha particles and atomic nuclei, and the resulting transmutations, can be studied atom by atom, because the energy produced in a single one of these reactions is enormous in comparison with the energy of chemical reactions, and manifests itself by the modifications it produces in the state of the millions of atoms in the appropriate parts of the detecting apparatus; and ingenious devices make it possible to amplify these modifications almost at will.

Thanks to his work with alpha particles, Rutherford was able to propound the first "model" of the atomic nucleus. He also discovered the diameter of this tiny space in which are enclosed the positive charges of the atom; a mere 1/10,000th part of the diameter of the atom itself. He effected the first transmutations. Also using alpha particles, Chadwick, repeating the experiments of Bethe and Becker and of the Joliot-Curies, identified the neutron. And the neutron in its turn served as an instrument of exploration and was all the more effective for the purpose because, having no electric charge, it was not kept away from the nucleus by the positive charge.

Today, physicists can avail themselves of much more effective probes than the alpha particles and neutrons of Rutherford and Chadwick; they can use cosmic radiation particles, and nuclei accelerated by giant modern accelerators. But before this stage had been reached it had become clear that the system formed by the nucleus and its attendant electrons was something very different from a sun and its planets, that this system was not governed by Newtonian mechanics, and that "we would have to alter our ideas on very fundamental points, on causality, for instance, and even on the nature of the objectivity of parts of the physical world." This brings us to Oppenheimer's exposition of the quantum revolution, which is the subject of the third and fourth lectures, *A Science in Change* and *Atom and Void in the Third Millennium*.

Oppenheimer was privileged to experience at first hand, in British and German universities, that great adventure of the human mind, and his description of it strikes a lyrical and almost religious note. Here we can glimpse the whole difference between science in the making, the new theory flowing like molten matter in the crucible of mathematical formulas, and science ready-made, old science, the consolidated structure of the theory which is handed down by teachers who themselves received it from other teachers.

The experience of the original discoverers of the atomic nucleus—and here we must use the word experience almost in its mystical sense—cannot be communicated. Nor, in these lectures, says Oppenheimer, can there be any attempt to give anything like a full explanation of what was discovered; his listeners and readers lack the necessary training. What hope remains for them? "We must talk of our subject not as a community of specialized scientists but as men concerned with understanding, through analogy, description, and an act of confidence and trust, what other people have done and thought and found. So men listen to accounts of soldiers returning from a campaign of unparalleled hardship and heroism, or of explorers from the high Himalayas, or of tales of deep illness, or a mystic's communion with his God. Such stories tell little of what the teller has to tell. They are the threads which bind us in community and make us more than separate men."

How are we to interpret such a passage as this? Does it express a haughty sense of superiority, a lack of confidence in the intellectual capacity of the layman? Surely, rather, it has a tragic undertone; a sense of isolation, a wish to communicate with ordinary people, to commune with them. For we find, indeed, that after declaring that science cannot be made clear for the general public, Oppenheimer undertakes to depict Rutherford's "planetary" atomic model—an exceedingly small, positively charged nucleus, surrounded at a great distance by negative charges—and to explain the difficulties which this conception encountered from the start.

If it were true that the electron revolved around the nucleus as a planet revolves around the sun, its orbit should become more or less rounded, or more or less elongated, when the nucleus was bombarded. Yet nothing of the kind takes place. The movement of the electron does not accord with Newtonian mechanics. Nor does it confirm Clerk Maxwell's laws. Elementary electromagnetic theory states that when a charge moves in anything but a straight line, it sends out electromagnetic radiations and, in so doing, gradually loses energy. Within a very short time (less than a millionth of a second) the radiation of the electron ought to descend through the whole gamut of frequencies, and the electron itself, as it progressively loses energy, ought to come closer and closer to the nucleus and finally become part of it.

But this, again, is observed not to happen. Hydrogen atoms, when they are undisturbed, are stable and identical; they send out no radiations and they last indefinitely. When disturbed, atoms do sometimes radiate, but only on certain definite frequencies which are specific to the various elements respectively; if they are probed with a stream of electrons they may absorb some of the energy of the electrons, but only in definite quantities and not in a random way; and "when an atom is irradiated by light, an electron will be ejected, if and only if the energy of that light exceeds a certain minimum known as the photoelectric threshold." It was in terms of these facts that Niels Bohr revised Rutherford's atomic model and Einstein and Planck laid the foundations of quantum theory. The understanding of microphysical phenomena was henceforth to demand that traditional ideas be transcended. When we disturb an atom, an electron passes from one energy-level to another without our being able to give a concrete description of the transition in terms of the movement of matter. The future behavior of atoms can be calculated in terms of probability, but cannot be predicted in detail with regard to any one atom. "We saw in the very heart of the physical world an end of that complete causality which had seemed so inherent a feature of Newtonian physics."

Yet that physics continues to hold good for the macrophysical world, the world of machines and bullets and stars. How can our familiar knowledge of that world be reconciled with the new physics? By means of the principle of correspondence. In the formulation of this principle "the key is the quantum of action, whose finiteness characterizes the new features of atomic physics. . . . The physicist says that, where actions are large compared to the quantum of action, the classical laws of Newton and Maxwell will hold. What this tends to mean in practice is that when mass and distances are big compared to those of the electron and the atom's size, classical theory will be right. Where energies are large and times long compared to atomic energies and times, we shall not need to correct Newton. Where this is so, the statistical laws of atomic physics will lead to probabilities more like certitudes, and the acausal features of atomic theory will be of no moment, and in fact lost in the lack of precision with which questions about large events will naturally be put."

But the reversal of old ideas went further than this.

After Einstein had discovered that light was emitted in the form of discontinuous (discrete) packets of energy, it seemed impossible to reconcile this conception with the one universally accepted since Maxwell's day, namely that light consists of a series of waves. Discontinuity suggests the existence of particles of light (photons); yet the phenomenon of interference, which is so familiar in connection with light, is exactly similar to that produced by waves on the surface of a lake. Moreover, the energy of any photon is equal to the product of the quantum of action (Planck's constant) by the frequency of the photon, and the second of these two magnitudes implies that light is wavelike in nature. But how can light particles be waves at the same time as they are particles? De Broglie eliminated the contradiction by postulating that with every particle (not only the photon) a wave' was associated. This holds good of the electron, the proton, the neutron and even the atom. It would even, says Oppenheimer, "be true of large objects also were it not that their wave length is small, because of smallness of Planck's constant, and becomes insignificant compared with their dimensions and with any practical possibility of determining their location and outline."

It was Schrödinger who formulated this generalization mathematically, and in so doing brought wave mechanics to birth. Its theoretical development, and also the difficulties thrown up by experiment, led to ideas more disconcerting still. The waves of this new mechanics are much more abstract than those encountered in earlier physics. The study and interpretation of them lead only to statistical affirmations: there is no certainty, but only such and such a degree of probability, that at a given point in space and time we shall encounter an electron. In addition, the more exactly we know the velocity of an electron, the less exactly do we know its position: and conversely. Heisenberg expressed this uncertainty relationship in mathematical form. We have traveled a long way from Newtonian mechanics: the very nature of the universe, not merely inadequate information, makes it impossible for us to define all aspects of a given system in a given instance. Thus in addition to the principle of correspondence, we have to admit that of complementarity; the state (energy level) of an electron, and its orbit, are complementary notions: "Where one applies the other cannot be defined, and for a full description we must be able to use now one, now the other, depending on the observation and the questions that we put."

Oppenheimer puts us on guard against the conclusion which common sense might lead us to draw from this, and which has been drawn by some philosophers. The atomic world has not shed its objective reality. But that world, the world of nuclear events, becomes accessible to us only because we transform our observation of it into "some large-scale happening—some flash of light, some triggering of a circuit, some pointing of a pointer on the dial of an instrument." And the nature of the experiment determines that of the property observed and measured, since, inherently, we are not in a position to observe all the properties at once.

Oppenheimer adds that "one could go much further in describing this discipline [quantum physics], even without mathematics; but the words would before long become cumbersome and unfamiliar and almost a misinterpretation of what in mathematical terms can be said with beauty and simplicity."

Here, nevertheless, are a few of the consequences of the new physics.

Probability having taken the place occupied, in classical physics, by causality, it becomes possible for some highly improbable phenomena to occur. Thus, in masses of stellar matter (in the sun, for example), "nuclei having only very moderate energy occasionally come into contact and react." This is, as yet, only a conjecture. But the capture of wandering neutrons by the nuclei of uranium 235, which is not conjectural, is explained by the fact that interaction of the particles takes place in some cases "over distances characterized not by their dimensions but by their wave length." And finally, as Oppenheimer explains in a passage already quoted here (pp. 31-32), the very notion of the identity of a particle becomes questionable, except in certain special cases.

In the fifth lecture the concept of complementarity is further illustrated, extended and defined. The title, *Uncommon Sense,* justifies the title of the series as a whole, and is no doubt intended to indicate a climax in the argument. The philosophical or imaginative passages in the lecture are less remarkable for intellectual rigor than the preceding lectures, but tell us correspondingly more about the author's intellectual attitude, his *Weltanschauung*.

Every human action or creation is transitory. "The day will come when our race is gone." Yet this truth is not sufficient for us to live by: "No man . . . thinks wholly in these terms. His acts, his thoughts, what he sees of the world around him—the falling of a leaf or a child's joke or the rise of the moon—are part of history; but they are not only part of history; they are a part of becoming and of process, but not only that: they partake also of the world outside of time; they partake of the light of eternity."

These two approaches to the real world, the temporal and the timeless, neither of which can be reduced to the other, may be regarded as forming a complementarity—in the same sense as, in physics, observations of the position and impulsion of a particle are complementary to each other.

Oppenheimer emphasizes more than once that this impossibility of observing simultaneously the position and energy of an atomic system does not proceed from anything inadequate in the procedure of observation: "It is not only that when we have made an observation on a system and determined, let us say, its position, we do not know its impulse. That is true, but more than that is true. We could say that we know the position of that system and that it may have any one of a number of different impulses. If we try on that basis to predict its behavior as a sort of average behavior of all objects which have the measured position and which have different and unmeasured impulses, and work out the average answer according to Newton's laws, we get a result that is wholly at variance with what we find in nature. This is because of the peculiar property, which has no analogue in the mechanics of large objects, of interference between waves representing the consequences of assuming one impulse and those of assuming another. We are not, that is, allowed to suppose that position and velocity are attributes of an atomic system, some of which we know and others of which we might know but do not. We have to recognize that the attempt to discover these unknown attributes would lose for us the known; that we have a choice, a dis-junction; and that this corresponds to the different ways we can go about observing our atom or experimenting with it.

"We have a state of affairs completely defined by the nature of the observation and by its outcome—the nature determining what properties of the system will be well defined in the state and what poorly."

We must, however, avoid the error of concluding from this that the state of affairs is merely subjective. On the contrary: "This state is objective. We can calculate its properties, reproduce it with similar atoms on another occasion, verify its properties and its ways of change with time. There is no element of the arbitrary or subjective." The difference is just that the state cannot be described in terms of classical mechanics, and that its properties possess complementarity.

Common sense is at a loss here simply because its familiar notions are derived from the world of large objects. "Common sense is wrong only if it insists that what is familiar must reappear in what is unfamiliar." Its notions are valid in their own sphere; and in any case we still use them in experimentation, when, for example, we note the movement of a needle on a dial, a movement which is part of the macrophysical world, where the uncertainties of the microphysical universe make no difference.

So we must not condemn common sense as an inadequate instrument for dealing with reality because it believes, for instance, that every object must have an ascertainable position and velocity. This conceptual inheritance does not apply to the microphysical world now being explored by science. It still holds good for the world of large objects. In this context, Oppenheimer demolishes in a few words the metaphysical generalizations of those philosophers who have thought to establish free will on the foundation of Heisenberg's uncertainty principle.

It should be noted in passing that Oppenheimer's exposition, which conforms rigorously to the principles of quantum mechanics, would not be unreservedly accepted by all physicists. The great Einstein admitted only unwillingly, as if contesting every inch of ground, the idea that it is possible for natural phenomena to be acausal and fundamentally unpredictable. At the back of his mind there was always the hope and conviction that the principle of uncertainty which had been introduced into modern physics was only provisional, something which would be unnecessary when the edifice of knowledge became more complete. Oppenheimer himself has drawn attention to this attitude of Einstein's in the preface he contributed to a biographical dictionary, *Jews in the World of Science,* where he pays admiring and moving homage to the creator of relativity theory. And at the present time we find M. Louis de Broglie, the father of wave mechanics, cogitating on the nature of indeterminism and encouraging the theoretical researches of younger scientists who are trying to re-establish the identity of particles or to reinstate causality in microphysical events.

Returning to Oppenheimer, we observe that after condemning the metaphysical exploitation of complementarity, he borrows analogies from other branches of science in an attempt to clarify the difficulties presented by that concept to the reader whose mind is shackled by common sense thinking. "We interpret the temperature of a gas, for instance, in terms of the average kinetic energy of its molecules, and the pressure as the average of the forces exerted by the collision of these molecules on the surface of the container. This description in terms of averages, embodying as part of itself our ignorance of the detailed state of affairs, is thus in some sense complementary to a complete dynamic description in terms of the motion of the individual molecules. In this sense kinetic theory and dynamics are complementary.

"But" (he goes on) "the analogy to atomic complementarity is only partial. . . ." A better parallel can be found in biology: just as there are certain events which the physicist cannot observe without modifying them, so there are processes, such as the redistribution of genes in the nuclei of dividing cells, which the biologist cannot study without interfering with the path the process normally takes.

Again, although we can describe the phenomena of consciousness, and although enormous progress has been made in the physiology of the sense organs and of the brain, "it seems rather unlikely that we shall be able to describe in physico-chemical terms the physiological phenomena which accompany a conscious thought, or sentiment, or will."

Similarly, complementarity can be seen in the relation between affective and intellectual life, and between free will and determinism in our actions.

Even if the progress of science makes it possible one day
to give a physico-chemical description of the phenomena of
consciousness, such a description "will be as irrelevant to the
acts of decision and the castings of the will as are the
trajectories of molecules to the entropy of a gas. To be
touched with awe, or humor, to be moved by beauty, to make
a commitment or a determination, to understand some truth
—these are complementary modes of the human spirit. All
of them are part of man's spiritual life. None can replace
the others, and where one is called for the others are in
abeyance."

The sixth and last lecture, *The Sciences and Man's Community,* sketches a panorama of contemporary science, accompanied by moral reflections pitched in a somewhat American key. One leading idea emerges: the great change im-
posed on humanity by the torrential forward movement of
science and technology. This revolution is as radical as that
which is sometimes produced in the life of a nation and a
people by an overwhelming military defeat. The knowledge
and the concepts which an individual acquires at school are
inadequate to the problems he will find himself facing in
adult years.

"The notion of universal knowledge has always been an
illusion; but it is an illusion fostered by the monistic view of
the world in which a few great central truths determine in
all its wonderful and amazing proliferation everything else
that is true." Today, the picture is very different. Science has
become so rich and various, so fluid and fast-moving, that
no individual mind is capable of embracing the whole of it.
"We know that we are ignorant; we are well taught it, and
the more surely and deeply we know our own job the better
able we are to appreciate the full measure of our pervasive
ignorance."

But we have one compensation: "Although we are sure not
to know everything and rather likely not to know very much,
we can know anything that is known to man, and may, with
luck and sweat, even find out some things that have not before been known to him." This "open access to knowledge" is
ensured by the social order characteristic of Great Britain
and the United States, with their freedom of speech and
freedom of association. At this point Oppenheimer aims a
powerful attack on the form of modern tyranny which calls

itself "by the very name of a belief in community"; and he gives a curious definition of Communism as "the belief that all communities are one community; that all truth is one truth; that all experience is compatible with all other; that total knowledge is possible; that all that is potential can exist as actual." This passage takes on a bitter flavor if one remembers that, at the very moment when Oppenheimer was reading it in front of a B.B.C. microphone, his condemnation on the grounds of suspected sympathy and complicity with Communism was waiting for him in Washington.

THE OPEN MIND

These philosophical and political views are set out at greater length in *The Open Mind,* Oppenheimer's second collection of essays intended for the lay public. This volume is less of a unity. Of the eight lectures it contains, the first four are concerned primarily with nuclear weapons, with the problem of their international control, and with United States policy in the nuclear field. These four lectures were delivered to different audiences, at considerable intervals of time. Their special interest is the light they throw on the history of the nuclear armaments race and the part played in it by Oppenheimer, a history outlined in the first part of the present work.

The fifth lecture, *Physics in the Contemporary World,* brings us somewhat closer to the general question of the relation between science and civilization. Something is said of the latest advance in nuclear physics, advances achieved partly by the use of giant accelerators; and an attempt is made to define the responsibility of the scientist in the contemporary world. Is the scientist responsible for the destructive use which society makes of his discoveries? No, for his task is to enrich knowledge, not to conduct the affairs of the community or the state. The author unfolds a somewhat original and probably fruitful idea: it is from the scientist's way of life, his rational attitude toward reality, that society should seek instruction and example. Serenity, freedom from the spirit of authority, rationality, the habit of collective endeavor, these are the distinguishing qualities of the scientific life; they should be applied in other fields as well, and make their contribution to the shaping of a higher form of civilization.

The sixth lecture, *The Encouragement of Science,* delivered to an audience of high school students, is a eulogy of the free spirit, the spirit which nourishes science and holds the promise of a better life for mankind: "There is no place for dogma in science. The scientist is free to ask any question, to doubt any assertion, to seek for any evidence, to correct any error. Where science has been used in the past to erect a new dogmatism, that dogmatism has found itself incompatible with the progress of science; and in the end, the dogma has yielded, or science and freedom have perished together." This is a profession of faith which might well be made better known today in any of the countries which in this same lecture—delivered in 1950—Oppenheimer described as being "plunged in darkness."

The seventh lecture, *The Scientist in Society,* addressed to a meeting of the Association of Princeton Graduate Alumni at Princeton, New Jersey, is a somewhat loosely connected review of several recurrent themes in Oppenheimer's thinking, in particular the universality of science. Under this aspect, the march of knowledge displays two opposite tendencies. On the one hand, scientific disciplines are becoming more and more diverse; specialization has become so intense that the scientist no longer knows what is going on outside his own speciality. Oppenheimer himself owns to having no more than a superficial idea of what is being done "in other parts of the house called science." But side by side with this increasing diversification there is a contrary tendency, which brings unity where previously there were rigidly divided compartments. Thus the theory of electricity has joined hands with that of light, quantum theory with valency theory. We may add—though perhaps Oppenheimer was not quite in a position to do so in 1953—that biology is now establishing a firm link with electronics.

The scientist's ignorance in fields other than his own speciality constitutes a problem. So does the ignorance of people in general with respect to the progress of knowledge, and, above all, their ignorance with respect to the human value, the potential human impact, of scientific experience. "The experience of science—to stub your toe hard and then notice that it was really a rock on which you stubbed it—this experience is something that is hard to communicate by popularization, by education, or by talk. It is almost as hard to tell a man what it is like to find out something new about the world as it is to describe a mystical experience to a chap who has never had any hint of such an experience."

Although it was read under rather different circumstances —as part of the celebration of Columbia University's Bicentennial, in 1954—the last paper, *Prospects in the Arts and Sciences,* is almost a continuation and expansion of the one immediately preceding it. It concludes with a parallel between the condition of the artist and that of the scientist. Both "live always at the edge of mystery, surrounded by it; both always, as the measure of their creation, have had to do with the harmonization of what is new with what is familiar, with the balance between novelty and synthesis, with the struggle to make partial order in total chaos. They can, in their work and in their lives, help themselves, help one another and help all men."

Anyone looking for a coherent system of thought in these lectures by Oppenheimer would perhaps be disappointed at encountering a certain amount of confusion and contradiction. But it would be unjust to level this as a reproach at a writer who makes a firm, total rejection of dogmatism in all its forms, and who, almost painfully eager to apprehend every aspect of reality, is never afraid to remind himself of the principle of complementarity and, if necessary, to apprehend aspects which appear to cancel each other out. One might see in this a certain dilettantism of the intellect; a description which fits Oppenheimer well enough, provided it is used without any pejorative intention. Apart from its political aspects, which one has the right to reject, and which are in any case bound up with the most contentious side of his life history, Oppenheimer's thinking has the merit of formulating, in a clear and intellectually exhilarating way, various crucial problems in an epoch of which we can truly say that it has created more questions than it has succeeded in answering.

Princeton

THE INSTITUTE OF ADVANCED STUDY

IN 1947, Robert Oppenheimer was appointed director of the Institute of Advanced Study at Princeton; a remarkable man for a remarkable post.

The Institute was founded some thirty years ago. Scholars and scientists come from all over the world to work there; in academic circles it enjoys a worldwide reputation. But the general public has very little idea of what goes on there. This is not surprising. The aim of the Institute's administrators is to provide an ideal setting in which leading exponents of all the scientific or scholarly disciplines can pursue their work in a secluded, peaceful atmosphere which favors concentration.

The Institute is not a curiosity—a collection of some of the world's finest living brains, a showcase. Nor is it an ivory tower. It is a harbor, a place of retreat which possesses a special symbolic value in these troubled and troubling times of ours. Just as the religious believer draws comfort from the knowledge that there are contemplative orders engaged in perpetual prayer, so too the man of study, and indeed any man, can derive a feeling of support from the knowledge that at Princeton outstanding men, in many cases men of genius, are working in full liberty in their chosen fields, laboring to augment the sum of discovery and advance the frontiers of human thought.

167

For that is what is expected of residents and visitors at Princeton: thought. They are not asked to concern themselves with the practical consequences of whatever they may discover. Their loyalty is to pure science and theoretical inquiry. As Dr. Abraham Pais, a member of the administrative faculty, has declared: "We are here to answer the question 'Why?', not the question 'What for?' "

Princeton, New Jersey, is a small town of 18,500 inhabitants, halfway between New York and Philadelphia. It is an island of green surrounded by an industrial ocean. The town owes its fame to its University and to several institutes of higher education, including technology, which are part of the University; and also to the Institute of Advanced Study, which many Europeans confuse with the University itself. Members of the Institute have the freedom of the University's magnificent library, and graduates of the University are sometimes invited to take part in research at the Institute or attend lectures given by visiting members. But the Institute and the University, organically and administratively, are separate entities.

Abraham Flexner was the man who won for Princeton, already famous for its University, the distinction of becoming the foremost intellectual center in America. Flexner, a great American teacher who revolutionized medical education in the United States, had never forgotten the atmosphere of the great German universities before the First World War. In 1928, when he was sixty-two and had just resigned his post as director of medical education, he came back to Europe and delivered a course of lectures at All Souls' College, Oxford.[1] The Oxford atmosphere won his heart. He took part in fruitful discussions among scholars from various countries. He appreciated the advantages which any scholar was bound to reap from an atmosphere created for studious concentration, and from friendly but utterly disinterested rivalry. He became urgently convinced of the need to found a small center in the United States, a place where men of science and men of letters could meet together and pursue their studies in complete freedom. He sensed the contribu-

[1] "The dons' college." Every Fellow of All Souls is a graduate; there are no undergraduates. [Tr.]

tion which such a foundation might make to the sum of human knowledge. Back in the States, he won the support of the founder of a chain of big stores, Louis Bamberger, and his sister, Mrs. Felix Fuld. In 1930 they offered him five million dollars to set up his center. Only one condition was attached to their generous gesture: the center must be in New Jersey. Flexner at once picked on Princeton as the ideal location, as his "guests" would be able to use the University library and laboratories. In 1931 the Mathematical School, the first item in the project, was opened: Flexner was its director, and among its earliest members was a star of the first magnitude, one of the most astonishing intellects the world has ever seen: Albert Einstein, who had just left Nazi Germany. Einstein spent the rest of his life at Princeton.

At first the Institute of Advanced Study was housed in the University's premises, but it soon had its own buildings in the vicinity. Its grounds cover 740 acres. The beauty of the countryside has a relaxing effect. In the early days a single building contained the offices, lecture rooms and restaurant; now there are five red-brick two-storey blocks clustered around Fuld Hall, a Georgian-style house which serves more or less as headquarters.

What these buildings hold are not lecture halls or laboratories but workrooms, specialized libraries, a few offices, and drawing rooms or sitting rooms where members can gather together or receive visitors. There are no formal courses of lectures at Princeton, but sometimes a member will give a talk if it seems to him that his work has reached a stage at which it might interest his colleagues. An annex has been put up for temporary guests. The permanent residents like to call it "the hotel for passing thinkers."

There are, in fact, two kinds of members at Princeton. Some live there all the time, others come for a limited period. A "faculty" of about twenty permanent members is responsible for running the Institute, under the director; this post has been occupied since 1947 by Robert Oppenheimer, who also teaches physics at the Institute. One of the functions of the faculty is to select the temporary members; many of these are professors taking a sabbatical year, or who have been given permission by their universities to detach themselves for a while in order to complete some piece of research on which they were already engaged. These temporary members are free to come and go as they wish. They work in their own private rooms, or in larger rooms if they want to collaborate with a group of colleagues. If they like, they can go and wander in the nearby woods in order to pursue their train of thought the better. Or they can just do nothing. They depend only on themselves; they are subject to no discipline whatsoever.

And they are financially as well as personally free. The Institute has an endowment from which it pays them a salary, and in many cases the salary is supplemented by a grant. This enables them to bring their families with them and settle in villas or modern apartments, either around the campus or in town.

Representatives of any nationality may be found among members of the Institute. Although there is no set quota, there are never more than 40% of Americans among them. All the members are doctors of philosophy or possess an equivalent degree. All are recognized figures in their own fields; many, indeed, have a reputation for outstanding brilliance. The twenty faculty members remain at the Institute until retirement; the temporary members, after a stay of variable length, mostly return to their own universities. Many are the institutions of higher education which pride themselves on the presence of ex-members of the Institute on their teaching staff. Similarly, the Institute is proud to see how many Nobel Prize winners come to work beneath its hospitable roof.

Almost every domain of thought is represented at Princeton. The Institute's two main divisions, the school of mathematics and the school of historical studies, have such diverse ramifications that no branch of intellectual activity is neglected. The members of this community are explorers, some of the present, others of the past; all of them work in complete intellectual freedom. There is no pressure on any of them to be anything less than fully objective.

The heart and soul of what goes on at the Institute is not to be measured in terms of published work, or of lectures delivered there or elsewhere, or of practical application. As Oppenheimer has said more than once, everyone who goes there is profoundly affected by making a certain discovery:

he finds out just how deeply he can be intellectually refreshed and replenished; and since most of the temporary members are professors or university lecturers, what they gain at Princeton is handed on to their pupils; so the influence of the Institute is always increasing.

Such unusual and various minds as Einstein and George Kennan, Joseph Neumann and T. S. Eliot, Niels Bohr, Arnold Toynbee the historian and Stromgren the astrophysicist, have found at Princeton an ambiance which encouraged them to develop what was best and most profound in their thinking. Released from workaday cares, free of administrative responsibilities, every scientist or thinker sheltered by the Institute pursues his own investigations. Often these are incomprehensible to the man in the next room. In the University observatory someone may be determining the age of a certain star, while an archaeologist in his study will be poring over finds from recent excavations in Greece.

Unique in its own kind, the Princeton Institute of Advanced Study gives a setting and an opening for the highest scholarship. It allows the pioneer researcher to feel free of what others may expect of him. And it does so because "the usefulness of the seemingly useless"—a favorite theme of Flexner's—has been so often and so amply proved.

(From material supplied by the United States Information Service, Paris.)

GLOSSARY

Glossary

Terms in common use, such as the names of the chemical elements, have been omitted from this glossary; so have all terms which are sufficiently explained in the text.

ACCELERATORS. Machines in which ions, that is to say particles bearing electric charges (electrons, protons, alpha particles), are accelerated by electric fields and reach a high degree of energy. In accelerators of the cyclotron type, the ions move in a circular orbit under the influence of a magnetic field perpendicular to their trajectory, and at each revolution electrodes accelerate their movement.

ALPHA RADIATION. Emission of helium nuclei.

BETA RADIATION. Emission of electrons (negative beta radiation) or positrons (positive beta radiation).

DIFFRACTION. A special case of interference. When a beam of light strikes a screen after passing through an aperture or along the surface of an obstacle, alternate bright and dark bands form a fringe around the image of the beam, encroaching on the surrounding unilluminated zone. This phenomenon, which is caused by the wave character of light, extends to all wave phenomena.

ELECTRON VOLT. A unit of energy used in nuclear physics. An electron volt represents the energy acquired by an electron in an electric field under the influence of a potential difference of 1 volt.

FREQUENCY. In a wave movement the number of periods per second. Frequency is equal to speed divided by wave length.

GAMMA RADIATION. Electromagnetic waves of shorter wave length than X rays.

175

GEIGER COUNTER. A device for detecting radioactivity by means of a tube filled with a non-conducting gas in which a discharge is produced by the movement of an ionized particle. The discharges can be amplified and counted.

INTERFERENCE. When the crest of one wave coincides with the trough of another of the same amplitude, the two waves cancel one another out at that point; conversely, the superimposition of one crest on another produces an augmented effect.

ISOTOPES. Atoms having the same atomic number (i.e. the same number of protons and the same number of electrons, and hence the same chemical properties) but different numbers of neutrons (and hence different atomic weights). Most substances existing in nature are associations of isotopes.

PLANCK'S CONSTANT. A universal constant which expresses the relationship between the frequency of a radiation and its quantum of energy.

POTENTIAL DIFFERENCE. A positive electric charge moves from points of higher potential to those of lower potential; potential difference is defined as the work done when a unit of positive charge moves from one point to another. The unit of potential difference is the volt.

SPIN. The revolution of a particle on its own axis, characterized by a quantified amount of movement. The unit of spin is Planck's constant divided by 2π.

STANDING WAVES. A phenomenon of interference, occurring when two waves of the same frequency and amplitude are propagated in opposite directions: at certain fixed, regularly spaced points the amplitude is zero (nodes); between every two nodes is a point of maximum amplitude (loop, or anti-node).

WILSON CLOUD CHAMBER. A chamber densely filled with water vapor, in which the trajectory of an ionized particle leaves a trail of condensation.

BIBLIOGRAPHY

Bibliography

BOOKS BY J. ROBERT OPPENHEIMER

Science and the Common Understanding. (The B.B.C. Reith Lectures, 1953). London: Oxford University Press, 1954; and New York: Simon and Schuster, 1954.

The Open Mind. New York: Simon and Schuster, 1955.

Jews in the World of Science. New York: World Publishers.

The Constitution of Matter. Oregon State System of Higher Education, 1956.

The New Weapon: "One World or None" (essays by various physicists, including J. R. Oppenheimer). New York: McGraw Hill, 1946.

CONTRIBUTIONS TO VARIOUS PERIODICALS

In French

L'Express: Speech delivered at the Congress for Cultural Freedom, Rheinfelden, October 15th, 1959.

Le Monde: "L'Arbre de la Science," May 31st, 1958.

In German

Naturwissenschaften: "Quantentheorie der kontinuierl. Absorptionspektr." (14, 1926).

Zeitschrift für den physikalischen und chemischen Unterricht: "Quantenmechanik der Richtungssentartung" (41, 1927). "Zerstreuung der Alpha-Teilchen" (43, 1927). "Strahlung der freien Elektronen im Coulombfeld" (55, 1929).

In English

Harper's Magazine, October, 1958: "The Tree of Knowledge."
Nature: "Quantum Theory and Intensity Distribution in Contin. Spectra" (118, 1926).
Proceedings Cambridge Philosophical Society: "Quantum Theory of Vibrat., Rotat. Bands" (23, 1926). "Quantum Theory of the Polarization of Impact Radiation" (13, 1927).
Proceedings National Academy of Science U.S.A.: "Quantum Theory of the Auto-Electric Field Currents" (14, 1928). "Quantum Theory of the Ramsauer Effect" (14, 1928).
Bulletin of Atomic Scientists: "Fateful Decision" (The H-Bomb), March 1950. "Encouragement of Science," January 1951. "Comments on the Military Value of the Atom," February 1951. "Atomic Weapons and American Policy," July 1953. "Science and Our Times," 1956. "An Inward Look," March 1958.
Review of Modern Physics: "Discussion on the Disintegration and Nuclear Absorption of Mesons," Vol. 21, p. 31 (1949).
Chemical and Engineering News: "Future of Atomic Energy. Atomic Explosives," Vol. 24, p. 1350 (1946).
Foreign Affairs: "International Control of Atomic Energy" (January 1948).
New York Times Magazine: "The Atom Bomb as a Great Force for Peace," June 9th, 1946.
Proceedings of the American Philosophical Society: "Symposium on Atomic Energy and its Implications. J.R.O.: Atomic Weapons," Philadelphia, Pa., U.S.A. (1946).

"PHYSICAL REVIEW"

Three Notes on the Quantum Theory of Aperiodic Effects. Vol. 31, p. 66 (1928).
On the Quantum Theory of the Capture of Electrons. Vol. 31, p. 349 (1928).
On the Quantum Theory of Electronic Impacts. Vol. 32, p. 361 (1928).
Note on the Theory of the Interaction of Field and Matter. Vol. 35, p. 461 (1930).
On the Theory of Electrons and Protons. Vol. 35, p. 562 L (1930).
Two Notes on the Probability of Radioactive Transition. Vol. 35, p. 939 (1930).
Note on the Statistics of Nuclei (J. R. Oppenheimer and P. Ehrenfest). Vol. 37, p. 333 A (1931).

Relativistic Theory of the Photoelectric Effect (J. R. Oppenheimer and Harvey Hall). Vol. 38, p. 57 (1931).

Note on Light Quanta and the Electromagnetic Field. Vol. 38, p. 725 (1931).

On the Range of Fast Electrons and Neutrons (J. R. Oppenheimer and J. F. Carlson). Vol. 38, p. 1786 (1931).

Impacts of Fast Electrons and Magnetic Neutrons (J. R. Oppenheimer and J. F. Carlson). Vol. 41, p. 763 (1932).

The Disintegration of Lithium by Protons. Vol. 43, p. 380 (1933).

On the Production of the Positive Electron (J. R. Oppenheimer and M. S. Plesset). Vol. 44, p. 53 (1933).

On the Theory of the Electron and Positive (J. R. Oppenheimer and W. H. Furry). Vol. 45, p. 245 (1934).

Production of Positives by Nuclear Gamma Rays (J. R. Oppenheimer and Leo Nedelsky). Vol. 45, pp. 283-343 (1934).

On the Limitations of the Theory of the Positron (J. R. Oppenheimer and W. H. Furry). Vol. 45, p. 903 L (1934).

On the Scattering of the Gamma Rays (J. R. Oppenheimer and C. C. Lauritsen). Vol. 46, p. 80 (1934).

Are the Formulae for the Absorption of High Energy Radiations Valid? Vol. 47, p. 44 (1935).

Note on Charge and Field Fluctuations. Vol. 47, p. 144 (1935).

Note on the Production of Pairs by Charged Particles. Vol. 47, p. 146 (1935).

The Disintegration of the Deuteron by Impact. Vol. 47, p. 845 (1935).

Note on the Transmutation Function for Deuterons (J. R. Oppenheimer and M. Phillips). Vol. 48, p. 500 (1935).

On the Elementary Interpretation of Showers and Bursts. Vol. 50, p. 389 A (1936).

The Density of Nuclear Levels. Vol. 50, p. 391 A (1936).

On Multiplicative Showers (J. R. Oppenheimer and J. F. Carlson). Vol. 51, p. 220 (1937).

The Disintegration of High Energy Protons (G. Nordheim, L. W. Nordheim, J. R. Oppenheimer and R. Serber). Vol. 51, p. 1037 (1937).

Note on the Nature of Cosmic-Ray Particles (J. R. Oppenheimer and J. Sorber). Vol. 41, p. 1113 L (1937).

Note on Nuclear Photoeffect at High Energies (F. Kalckar, J. R. Oppenheimer and R. Serber). Vol. 52, p. 271 (1937).

Note on Resonances in Transmutations of Light Nuclei (F. Kalckar, J. R. Oppenheimer and R. Serber). Vol. 52, p. 279 (1937).

Note on Boron Plus Proton Reactions (J. R. Oppenheimer and R. Serber). Vol. 53, p. 636 (1938).

On the Stability of Stellar Neutron Cores (J. R. Oppenheimer and R. Serber). Vol. 54, p. 540 (1938).
On Massive Neutron Cores (J. R. Oppenheimer and G. M. Volkoff). Vol. 55, p. 374 (1939).
On Continued Gravitational Contraction (J. R. Oppenheimer and H. Snyder). Vol. 56, p. 455 (1939).
On Pair Emission in the Proton Bombardment of Fluorine. Vol. 56, p. 1066 (1939).
Production of Soft Secondaries by Mesotrons (J. R. Oppenheimer, H. Snyder and R. Serber). Vol. 57, p. 75 (1940).
On the Applicability of Quantum Theory to Mesotron Collisions. Vol. 57, p. 353 A (1940).
On the Spin of the Mesotron. Vol. 59, p. 462 (1941).
On the Selection Rules in Beta-Decay. Vol. 59, p. 908 (1941).
On the Interaction of Mesotrons and Nuclei (J. R. Oppenheimer and Julian Schwinger). Vol. 60, p. 150 (1941).
Internal Conversion in Photosynthesis. Vol. 60, p. 158 (1941).
The High Energy Soft Component of Cosmic Rays. Vol. 60, p. 159 A (1941).
Multiple Production of Mesotrons by Protons. Vol. 60, p. 159 A (1941).
On the Internal Pairs from Oxygen. Vol. 60, p. 164 (1941).
Pair Theory of Meson Scattering (J. R. Oppenheimer and E. C. Nelson). Vol. 61, p. 202 (1942).
Reaction of Radiation on Electron Scattering and Heitler's Theory of Radiation Damping (J. R. Oppenheimer and H. A. Bethe). Vol. 70, p. 451 (1946).
Multiple Production of Mesons (H. W. Lewis, J. R. Oppenheimer and S. A. Wouthuysen). Vol. 73, p. 127 (1948).
Note on Simulated Decay of Negative Mesons (S. T. Epstein, R. J. Finkelstein and J. R. Oppenheimer). Vol. 73, p. 1140 (1948).

BOOKS ABOUT OPPENHEIMER

Robert Jungk, *Brighter than a Thousand Suns.* London: Gollancz, in association with Hart-Davis, 1958.
J. and S. Alsop, *We Accuse; the Story of the Miscarriage of American Justice in the Case of J. Robert Oppenheimer.* New York: Simon and Schuster, 1954.
C. Curtis, *The Oppenheimer Case.* New York: Simon and Schuster.
Kugelmass, *J. R. Oppenheimer and the Atomic Story.* New York: Messner, 1953.
U.S. *Atomic Energy Commission: In the Matter of J. R. Oppenheimer. (Transcript of hearings before Personnel Security Board.)* Washington, D.C., 1954. (The verbatim report of the Oppenheimer "trial.")
Haakon Chevalier, *L'Homme qui voulait être Dieu* (The Man

Who Wanted To Be God). Paris: Editions du Seuil, 1960. [A novel, largely autobiographical, in which Oppenheimer appears under the name of Bloch.]

BACKGROUND WORKS ON CONTEMPORARY PHYSICS, INCLUDING QUANTUM THEORY, WAVE MECHANICS AND NUCLEAR ENERGY

A. Einstein, and Infield, L. *The Evolution of Physics.* University Press: Cambridge, 1938.

George Gamow, *Atomic Energy in Cosmic and Human Life.* University Press: Cambridge, 1947.

M. Planck. *Scientific Autobiography and Other Papers.* Trans. F. Gaynor. London: Williams & Norgate, 1950.

INDEX

Index